NDS

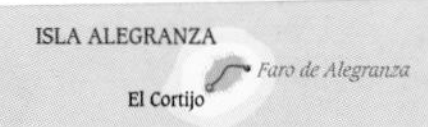

Atlantic Ocean

Miguel Ángel Cabrera Pérez

VISIT

NATIVE FLORA OF THE CANARY ISLANDS

EVEREST

Editorial coordination: Jaime Díaz

Author: Miguel A. Cabrera Pérez

Photographs: Rafael C. Rodríguez Santana and Miguel A. Cabrera Pérez

Layout: Mercedes Fernández

Digital image processing: Marcos R. Méndez

Cartography: Francisco A. Morais (© Everest)

Cover design: Alfredo Anievas

Translation: EURO:TEXT (Martin Gell)

Carretera León-La Coruña, km 5 - LEÓN
ISBN: 84-241-3555-5
Legal deposit: LE. 550-1999
Printed in Spain - Impreso en España

EDITORIAL EVERGRÁFICAS, S. L.
Carretera León-La Coruña, km 5
LEÓN (Spain)

FOREWORD

Rising up amidst the waters of the Atlantic Ocean, the Canary Islands constitute the point at which in the course of time the cultural and biological heritage of three continents has come to converge. Furthermore, with regard to the natural life forms that exist on the archipelago, the Canaries are a living testimony of the biological evolution that has taken place in this particular corner of the Earth. This should come as no surprise, however, for wherever the visitor may be on the islands, he is inevitably struck by the sheer wealth of the Canary flora, this being a land where numerous plant species that have vanished from all other continents are seen to thrive alongside other taxa that have evolved at a truly vertiginous pace.
Just a short distance of no more than thirty or forty kilometres separates the coastal environments from the mountain peaks on the highest Canary Islands, giving rise to a succession of spectacular changes in the prevailing flora, as the desert or subdesert formations are replaced by the plant formations typical of the high mountain terrain, the latter being preceded on the westernmost islands by the characteristic subtropical laurisilva woodlands. This variety of habitats and ecosystems found on the Canaries contains an enormous array of floral species marked by a high percentage of endemic taxa, a fact which makes the islands one of the most interesting regions of the world in terms of biodiversity.
A little interest is all it takes for one to become acquainted with the species that go to make up the singular ecosystems of these islands. Consequently, the aim of this book is no other than to promote the knowledge of the Canary flora amongst not only the local inhabitants but also the countless visitors who choose the archipelago as their holiday destination.
The book has been divided into two major sections, the first of which serves as an introduction which seeks to provide a succinct account of the importance of the Canary flora and its state of conservation, and also offers a brief description of the main plant communities to be found on the islands.
The second section of the book is devoted to the description of a selection of the most representative and frequently found species belonging to each of the principal Canary ecosystems. It also includes those species which, despite being relatively rare, are a fine illustration – on account of their beauty, scientific value or peculiarity – of the great wealth and variety of the flora that is endemic to the archipelago. The species have been arranged according to the plant communities in which they occur. For each individual taxon, both the scientific and common names are provided, along with a brief description of the plant's basic morphological attributes and details regarding its distribution and its traditional uses. Additionally, an indication is given as to the degree of rarity of each species and the particular level of protection it enjoys. The descriptions are accompanied throughout by photographs aimed at highlighting the most relevant morphological features of each plant in order that the latter may be identified as quickly and as easily as possible in natural conditions.
Lastly, we should like to acknowledge the great interest shown and the assistance afforded by our publishers Editorial Everest, the invaluable help and support provided by Carlos Samarín Bello, and furthermore to dedicate this book to Javier, Luisa, Julia and Montse, to whom we are indebted for their endless patience and understanding.

THE AUTHORS

Legend of Symbols Used

- Type of Endemic

C Canary Endemic

M Macaronesian Endemic

CA Canary-African Endemic

MA Macaronesian-African Endemic

- Biotype

Tree

Shrub

Small shrub, subshrub

Herbaceous plant

Climbing plant

Creeper

Succulent plant

Thorny

- Uses

Ornamental plant

Medicinal plant

Edible

Poisonous plant

Plant of value to forestry or used for traditional purposes

- Degree of Protection

Species enjoying protection under any form of legislation

- State of Conservation

Endangered species

INTRODUCTION

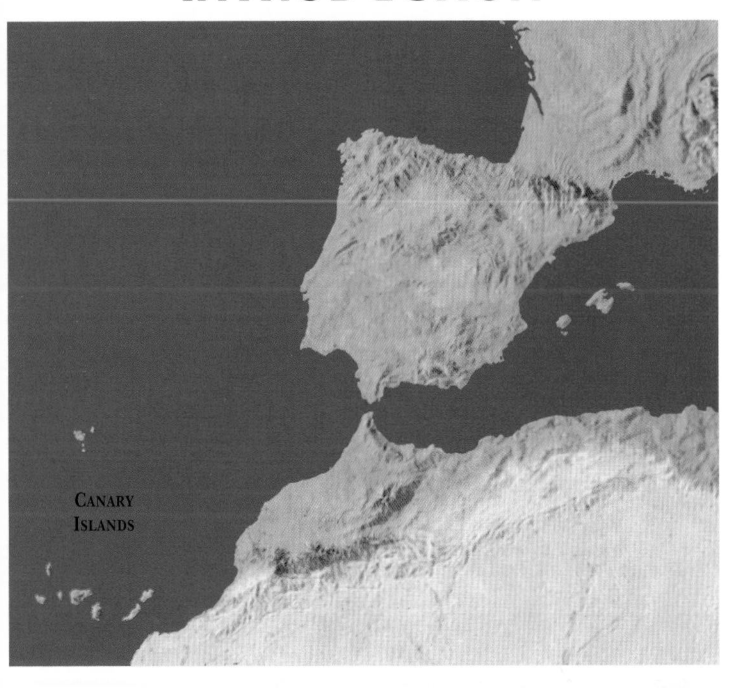

THE CANARY ISLANDS, A TRULY SINGULAR ARCHIPELAGO

The Canary Archipelago, situated to the north of the Tropic of Cancer, less than 150 kilometres from the African coast, comprises seven main islands (La Palma, El Hierro, La Gomera, Tenerife, Gran Canaria, Fuerteventura and Lanzarote), and a variety of islets and rocks (such as La Graciosa, Alegranza, Montaña Clara, Lobos, Roque del Este, Roque del Infierno). The Canaries are oceanic in nature, that is to say, they are islands that have emerged in the midst of the Atlantic Ocean as the result of volcanic activity and which geologically speaking have never been attached to the continental land mass. The said volcanic activity, which is to be held responsible both for the outcropping of the islands above the earth's surface and for the increase in their extension, has played a highly active role in the shaping of the Canary Islands as we know them today. This constructive mechanism has been counteracted by a series of intense erosion processes that have occurred between the successive cycles of volcanic activity. Indeed, erosion has gradually carved away at the original geological materials, giving rise to a number of highly varied geographical reliefs, the individual forms of which depend on the intensity and duration of its effects. Thus, in the westernmost islands we come across a rugged relief marked by deep ravines, great escarpments and cliffs that stand in sharp contrast with the predominantly smooth, rounded landforms characterising the older islands, such as Fuerteventura. Bearing in mind the varying ages of the different islands, which range from the 19 million years attributed to Lanzarote to the less than a million years assigned to El Hierro, it should come as no

surprise that the Canaries should display such enormous morphological contrasts - a diversity that is apparent both from one island to another and between the younger and older areas of a single island.
Furthermore, the geographical reality of the Canary Archipelago is determined by its subtropical position near to the African continent, one in which the islands are favourably influenced by the cool waters of the Canaries Current and the action of the Trade Winds. The resulting climatic conditions have led the Canary climate to be considered as one of the most benign in the world and explains why the archipelago is known as “the land of the eternal spring”. Moreover, the islands exhibit a high microclimatic variability that is associated with both their topography and altitude. Consequently, it is possible to witness at the same time snow on the mountain peaks, thick sea mists at medium heights and brilliant sunshine in coastal areas.
Together, the above-mentioned factors have conditioned what can be termed a singular, highly differentiated plant colonisation process and have governed the development of the different plant communities present on the archipelago, in such a way that today the islands constitute veritable natural laboratories in which one can study the formation processes of new species and gain valuable insight into the past history of the Earth.
Needless to say, the said features are not exclusive to the Canary Archipelago and are shared by other groups of islands in the East Atlantic Ocean. Indeed, from a biogeographical point of view, the Canaries belong to the so-called Macaronesian Region, which also includes the Azores, Madeira, Ilhas Selvagens and Cape Verde. Coined in the mid-19th century by Philippe Baker Webb, one of the leading authorities in the study of the flora of the Canary Islands, the term *Macaronesia* literally means “the Fortunate Isles”, having been derived from the Greek words *makaro* (“happy”) and *nesias* (“islands”). Today great controversy has arisen as to whether the Cape Verde Islands – and to a lesser extent the Azores – should be classified as pertaining to this region.

GENERAL CHARACTERISTICS OF THE FLORA AND VEGETATION OF THE CANARY ISLANDS

The origin of the flora of the Canary Islands

In order to fully understand the origin of the autochthonous flora of the Canary Islands, one has to take into account both the oceanic nature of the archipelago and the age of the latter. In this sense, the plant colonisation of the islands must have involved the plant formations that existed on the nearest continental territories as from the moment when each of the islands emerged. Accordingly, most authors recognise that the autochthonous vascular flora of the Canary Archipelago is derived from two major sources, namely the Mesogenous and African contingents.
The term Mesogenous contingent covers the flora that evolved along the shores of the former Ocean of Tethys, the present-day vestige of which is the Mediterranean Sea. This flora boasted both tropical and subtropical features and its original distribution area was severely reduced as a result of the various glacial periods that Europe underwent in the Quaternary. The elements of Canary plantlife that have their origin in this flora are to be found in the characteristic laurisilva woodlands of the archipelago, in the form of species such as the "acebiño" or Canary holly *(Ilex canariensis)*, the "til" *(Ocotea foetens)*, the "viñátigo" *(Persea indica)* or the laurel *(Laurus azorica)*.
On the other hand, amongst the different sources that go to make up the African contingent, we should highlight the one that specialists have dubbed "Rand Flora". Being as it is characteristic of arid and semiarid zones, this flora spread from South Africa to Northern Africa. It, too, was to experience a considerable reduction in its original distribution, which in this case was due to the processes of desertification that have befallen the African continent. As a result of their xerophile nature, the floristic components derived from this contingent are to be found in the low-lying, arid areas of the islands, their most striking representatives being the species belonging to the genera *Dracaena, Euphorbia, Aeonium* or *Ceropegia*.
From the original colonising species, by means of natural processes of differentiation and speciation, in the course of time new species have developed that are capable of occupying vacant niches and habitats, thereby giving rise to the most singular, richly varied flora to be seen today on the Canary Archipelago.

The importance of the flora of the Canary Islands

Oceanic islands are to be defined as enclaves whose major characteristic is that of their high biological diversity. Indeed, on a world-wide scale, a sixth of all land plant species are seen to occur in insular ecosystems. The Canary Archipelago is no exception to this rule, displaying as it does a richly varied flora, one which features a large number of endemic species. A clear illustration of this fact is given by the following two points:

• Despite occupying less than 1.5% of the total surface area of Spain, the Canary Islands account for over half the plant endemics to be found in this country.

• On comparing the islands with Great Britain, we find that although the latter boasts a surface area 34 times greater than that of the Canaries, it has just 16 endemic plants to its name, as opposed to the over five hundred such species that are present on the archipelago.

Underlying this relative abundance of endemic taxa are a series of different factors, of which we shall highlight the following:

• Owing to their insular nature, the Canaries exhibit a large number of relict species. These are species which, having formerly enjoyed a much wider distribution in other parts of the globe, are now restricted to the archipelago, where they have survived unaffected by the various climatic changes that have occurred in continental areas. Such species as these are classified as *palaeoendemics.*

• Secondly, the wide array of habitats and ecological niches resulting from the different environmental conditions prevailing in the Canaries (as regards rainfall, altitude, moisture, substrata, etc.) have favoured the processes of speciation via adaptive radiation, processes which are intensified and accelerated in cases of geographical isolation, since contact between similar taxa is avoided. The species derived from the said speciation processes are referred to as *neoendemics.*

The exact number of endemic taxa, however, is seen to vary from one plant group to another. Thus, the proportion of endemic species recorded for the algae stands at less than 9% and, similarly, no more than 10% of the fungi constitute taxa endemic to the archipelago. The same state of affairs is repeated in the case of the bryophytes, which reflect a low percentage of Canary or Macaronesian endemics (approximately 5.6%). Special mention, in this regard, has to be made of vascular plants (ferns, gymnosperms and angiosperms), a group which accounts for the greatest number of species that are unique to the Canaries. According to the latest calculations, the total number of species of this kind to be found on the Canary Archipelago amounts to 1,978. No less than 575 of these are endemic to the Macaronesian region, whilst 514 feature distributions that are restricted to the Canaries. What this implies is that in this case the percentage of Canary endemics is as high as 25.9%, of which 57% are exclusive to one island alone.

The relative floristic wealth of each of the islands is closely linked to factors such as surface area, altitude, age, and diversity of habitats, in such a way that the combination of these features will in each case determine the existence of a greater or lesser number of endemics. Thus, the island of Tenerife, which boasts the largest extension and the highest mountains of all the Canaries, displays a total of 1,370 species, of which approximately 54% are Macaronesian and/or Canary endemics. At the other end of the scale lie the islands of Lanzarote and Fuerteventura, which, being the oldest and least mountainous of the archipelago, afford the smallest percentage of Canary endemics.

Endangered species. Methods of protection provided for the wild flora of the Canary Islands

Over the last few decades, the Canary Archipelago has undergone a process of dramatic socio-economic development, one which has inevitably had a significant impact on the natural environment and the conservation of natural resources. The consequences of such growth on the Canaries are all the more drastic in light of the extreme fragility that characterises island ecosystems.
As a result of the intense exploitation of natural resources in the past and the great stress that the natural ecosystems of the Canary Islands are having to endure at present, a large number of the species that go to make up the local flora are in danger of extinction. Current estimations warn that the endangered species in the Canary Islands account for no less than 70% of the flora in danger of extinction in all Spain.
The most recent list assessing the state of conservation of the Canary flora species is that published in the *Libro Rojo de Especies Vegetales Amenazadas de las Islas Canarias (Red Book of Endangered Plant Species of the Canary Islands),* written in 1996 by Gómez Campo et al. This inventory uses the categories of rarity established by the International Union for Conservation of Nature and Natural Resources (IUCN) prior to their latest revision. Thus, the categories and definitions employed were as follows:

• **Endangered (E).** These are species that are clearly in danger of extinction and which are unlikely to survive if the causes of their reduction persist. Also included in this group are those species in which the number of individuals has decreased to a critical level or whose habitats have been drastically reduced.

• **Vulnerable (V).** This term is applied to those species that are deemed likely to become endangered in the near future if the current causes are allowed to continue. Also included here are those species, most or all of whose populations are undergoing a progressive reduction on account of their exploitation, the destruction of their habitat or other environmental changes.

• **Rare (R).** These are species featuring small world populations that cannot be included in the previous categories but which nevertheless are at risk. These taxa are generally confined to small geographical areas or habitats or display a wide distribution of small and isolated populations.

• **Insufficiently Known (K).** This category comprises those species that are suspected to belong to one of the above categories but about which there is a lack of information.

• **Out of danger (O).** This term refers to those species that have previously been included in one of the above categories but which are now deemed to be relatively safe as a result of the adoption of effective conservation measures or the elimination of the risk factors that had endangered their survival. This category was not used by the authors of the *Libro Rojo de Especies Vegetales Amenazadas de las Islas Canarias.*

• **Unendangered species.** Species that do not fit into any of the categories above; that is, ones for which no particular danger has been identified.

The said Red Book or *Libro Rojo* considered some 300 species appearing on the Canary Islands, of which it classifies 105 as being "in danger of extinction", 118 as "vulnerable", 57 as "rare", 8 "insufficiently known" and 12 as "unendangered". Such an analysis as this reflects the truly alarming situation facing the Canaries flora, one that has led to the adoption of a number of legal and administrative measures on both an international, national and regional scale; measures which together have laid the foundations for the protection and conservation of the islands' rich floristic heritage. The following are the principal protection regulations concerning wild flora species that apply to the Canary Archipelago:

• **Convention for the Conservation of the Wildlife and Natural Habitats of Europe** (Berne Agreement). Signed by Spain on 19th September 1979 and ratified on 13th May 1986, this agreement stipulates, in Chapter III on the Conservation of Species, that each state should adopt the appropriate legislative and regulatory measures needed to guarantee the conservation of the individual wild floral species which, listed in Annexe I of the agreement, are declared as meriting the strictest protection. The intentional picking, harvesting, cutting or uprooting of these plants is therefore to be prohibited, one possibility being to place a ban on the possession and marketing of the same.

• **Directive 92/43/EEC concerning the Conservation of the Natural Habitats and the Wild Fauna and Flora** (EC Habitats Directive). This European Directive was assimilated into the Spanish code of laws by means of Royal Decree 1997/1995, dated 7th December. The latter sets out a series of measures intended to help safeguard biodiversity in Spain by means of the conservation of natural habitats and wild fauna and flora. Annexe II of the said Directive lists animal and plant species that are of Community-wide importance and whose conservation requires the establishment of Special Conservation Areas. Indication is given of the species considered to be of priority interest, namely those whose conservation represents a particular responsibility for the European Union on account of the fact that a considerable proportion of their natural distribution area falls within Community territory. All in all, the provisions of the Directive affect a total of 66 species of the Canary Islands flora, half of which are classified as being priority cases.

• **National Catalogue of Endangered Species.** By virtue of Act of Parliament 4/1989, Chapter II, Title IV – concerning wild flora and fauna –, the categories into which endangered species are to be classified were established ("in danger of extinction", "vulnerable", "sensitive to habitat disturbance" and "of special interest") and the National Catalogue of

Endangered Species was created. In Royal Decree 439/1990, dated 30th March, which regulates the said National Catalogue of Endangered Species, only one species of the flora found on the Canary Archipelago appears as being "in danger of extinction", whereas in the Order of 9th July 1998, by means of which certain species were included in the National Catalogue of Endangered Species and others already appearing in the latter were re-classified, a total of 64 species belonging to the wild flora of the Canaries were assigned to the category "in danger of extinction". Thus, a large number of Canary Island species have been awarded the highest degree of protection contemplated under State legislation. According to the provisions of the latter, it is the duty of the relevant governmental authority to draw up a Recovery Plan for each of the species in question, in order that the necessary measures may be adopted to eliminate the danger threatening their survival. Moreover, the very fact that a given species is classified as "in danger of extinction" entails a series of generic prohibitions covering all non-authorised acts perpetrated upon it, such as cutting, felling, uprooting or the gathering of seed or pollen. Similarly, it is considered a very serious offence to either destroy, kill, damage, gather or commercialise those plants classified as "in danger of extinction", including their propagules and remains; it is likewise illegal to capture and exhibit them for commercial purposes or to use them for unauthorised naturalisation.

• **Order dated 20th February 1991 concerning the protection of wild vascular plant species in the Autonomous Community of the Canaries** (Flora Order). This Order contains three Annexes which set out various guidelines regarding the use and protection of wild flora species on the Canary Islands. Annexe I provides a list of the species enjoying strict protection, it being prohibited either to tear up, cut down or uproot the said plants or any part of them, or to deliberately destroy or disturb the latter, including their seeds, or to use them for commercial purposes. Annexe II records the protected species for which the above-mentioned uses and activities are subject to authorisation by the governmental body responsible for nature conservation. Lastly, Annexe III lists those species that can be used for certain purposes.

PRINCIPAL PLANT COMMUNITIES OF THE CANARY ISLANDS

Principal plant communities of the Canary Islands

The plant communities to be found on the islands can be divided into two basic categories:

• Those communities whose distribution is governed by climatic factors, in such a way that they are arranged altitudinally according to what many authors have referred to as *bioclimatic layers or zones*. Traditionally a total of 4 bioclimatic layers have been described for the archipelago (Infracanary, Thermocanary, Mesocanary and Supracanary), along with a number of variants that depend on precipitation levels (ombroclimates). Each one of these bioclimatic layers has its own particular range of plant communities, which together constitute what is termed a *vegetation layer or zone*. Thus, one may refer to the basal-layer vegetation characteristic of the Infracanary bioclimatic zone (featuring the spurge formations, *Euphorbia* spp.); the transition-layer vegetation pertaining to the dry Thermocanary zone (basically comprising the thermosclerophyllous woods); the subhumid montane-layer vegetation, which contains the formations called *fayal-brezal* and *laurisilva,* which together are known as *monteverde;* the dry montane-layer vegetation, dominated by pinewoods; and, lastly, the Supracanary layer vegetation, whose outstanding feature is the scrub that inhabits the mountain peaks.

• Representing a contrast to the above plant communities are the so-called azonal communities, whose distribution is conditioned not by the climate but by other considerations (such as edaphic and chemical factors). Amongst those communities that can be classified as being azonal are those found on the coasts (salt marsh, sand and coastal halophilic communities), as well as rock communities and those inhabiting recent volcanic lava flows or ravines (featuring "tarajales" or *Tamarix* spp. shrubs and "sauzales" or willow groves).

Coastal Halophilic Vegetation

The coastal halophilic communities of the Canaries are regarded as azonal ecosystems, governed as they are fundamentally by edaphic factors, and have to endure conditions of extreme hydric, thermal and salt stress, both in the soil and in the atmosphere. The following communities are worthy of special mention:

• **Halophilic belt communities.** This is the name given to those plant communities that are located on a narrow strip of the coast on all the islands of the archipelago. They are characterised by small-sized, shrubby plants affording low-percentage cover and are dominated by the following species: "lechuga de mar" *(Astydamia latifolia), Frankenia ericifolia,* "espinero" *(Lycium intricatum),* "salados" *(Schyzogyne sericea, S. glaberrima),* "uvilla de mar" *(Zygophyllum fontanesii),* "siemprevivas" *(Limonium pectinatum), Frankenia ericifolia,* "perejil de mar" *(Crithmum maritimum)* and "magarza de costa" *(Argyranthemum frutescens).* The characteristic features of the habitat of these species are the instability and the porosity of the terrain, as a result of which the communities are restricted to surfaces that have a lesser degree of inclination and display a certain level of soil retentivity or which are associated with basalt fissures.

• **Psammophilic communities.** This term refers to communities that have become established on accumulations of sand – either fixed sands or mobile dunes – and which are most widespread on the islands of Lanzarote, Fuerteventura and Gran Canaria. The most representative species of this type of plant community are the "balancón" *(Traganum moquinii), Chenoleoides tomentosa, Polycarpaea nivea, Polygonum maritimum, Euphorbia paralias* and *Salsola Kali.* Several endangered species are also to be found in these environments, such as *Lotus kunkelii, Convolvulus caput-medusae, Atractylis preauxiana* and *Lotus arinagensis.*

• **Salt-marsh communities.** Restricted as they are to only a small area of the islands, these communities characteristically develop over salt pools and feature a predominance of species of the Chenopodiaceae (Goosefoot) family, which are perfectly adapted in order to survive immersed in salt water. Particularly noteworthy are two species, *Sarcocornia fruticosa* and *Suaeda vermiculata.* The best examples of salt-marsh communities are found on Fuerteventura and the islet of Lobos.

ASTYDAMIA LATIFOLIA

Family
APIACEAE (PARSLEY)

Astydamia latifolia (L. fil.) Baill.
Spanish common name: LECHUGA DE MAR, SERVILLETA.

Astydamia latifolia.

This endemic of the Canary Islands and Northern Africa is the only species in its genus and is to be found throughout the archipelago, although it occurs less frequently on the islands lying farthest to the east. It is one of the most representative species of the coastal plant communities of the Canaries, particularly those gracing the northern shores, where it appears in association with species such as *Crithmum maritimum* (sea parsley, perejil de mar) or *Limonium pectinatum* (sempervivum). A small plant, it features fleshy erect greyish-green stems. It has fleshy, rather hard leaves which are the same colour as the stem and can reach a length of over 20 cm. These are wide-lobed, pinnate leaves whose petioles partially envelop the stem at their base. Its yellowish-green flowers have small petals and are grouped into umbel-type inflorescences that can measure up to 12 cm in diameter. Its flowering period lasts for several months, above all from December to April. In winter, the plant's canopy disappears, to subsequently grow back again from buds situated at ground level.

ARGYRANTHEMUM FRUTESCENS

Family
ASTERACEAE (DAISY)

Argyranthemum frutescens (L.) Sch. Bip.
Spanish common name: MAGARZA.

Argyranthemum frutescens.

This shrub boasts a wide distribution, appearing on all the islands of the archipelago except for Lanzarote and Fuerteventura. Characterised by its high morphological variability, a total of 7 different subspecies have been described. It is a densely branched, woody plant, which can reach a height of 60 cm. Its compound leaves, normally uni- or bipinnate, measure up to 8 cm in length, are dark green in colour and have a slightly fleshy consistency. Its flowers are arranged into heads with white ligules measuring up to 3 cm in diameter, both terminal and axillary. Examples of this species in flower can be found practically all year round. Traditionally its leaves have been used in infusions as a tonic for stomach upsets and as a means of relief for asthma-sufferers. Being as it is a species of high ornamental value, this plant is often seen in the parks and gardens of the Canary Islands. This species is included in Annexe II of the Order issued by the Autonomous Government of the Canaries regarding wildlife protection.

ATRACTYLIS ARBUSCULA

Family
ASTERACEAE (DAISY)

Atractylis arbuscula Svent. et Michaelis.
Spanish common name: PIÑA DE MAR.

Atractylis arbuscula.

Endemic to the Canary archipelago, this species is limited to two of the islands: the variety named *Atractylis arbuscula* var. *arbuscula,* appears on Lanzarote, whilst *Atractylis arbuscula* var. *schizogynophylla* is found at specific points along the northern coast of Gran Canaria. This is a robust, woody, shrub-like, densely branched plant that can reach a height of over 25 cm. It has greyish-hued, fine-haired lanceolate leaves and its pinkish flowers are arranged on a series of terminal flower heads. The characteristic habitat of *Atractylis arbuscula* is that of cliff areas and rocky slopes with a minimal amount of soil. Owing to the relative scarcity of its populations, this species is at present in a rather precarious situation and is considered to be in danger of extinction. Consequently, it is accounted for in all the regulations governing the protection of wild flora that are applicable to the Canary Islands. *Atractylis arbuscula* is listed in Annexe I of the Berne Agreement; it is classified as a Priority Species under the EC Habitats Directive; it ranks as a species "in danger of extinction" in the National Catalogue of Endangered Species; and is regarded as a species meriting strict protection within the Autonomous Community of the Canary Islands (Flora Order). This plant can be found in certain parks and gardens on the island of Lanzarote.

ATRACTYLIS PREAUXIANA

Family
ASTERACEAE (DAISY)

Atractylis preauxiana Sch. Bip.
Spanish common name: PIÑA DE MAR.

Atractylis preauxiana.

The distribution of this small shrub is confined to coastal areas of eastern and southern Gran Canaria and Tenerife. It can be distinguished from the previous species on account of its being a smaller-sized plant, ranging in height from 5 to 10 cm, and its oblanceolate leaves which, measuring up to 2 cm long and practically forming a basal rosette, feature rigid tips and slightly serrulate margins. Its flower heads display white ligules whose posterior surface is a violet hue. *Atractylis preauxiana* has a flowering period spanning the months of April and June. As is the case with *Atractylis arbuscula,* this plant is an endangered species, a situation which is owed above all to the rapid disruption of its natural habitat. Consequently it is also subject to the strict protection measures provided by the above-mentioned legislation.

SCHIZOGYNE SERICEA / SCHIZOGYNE GLABERRIMA

Family
ASTERACEAE (DAISY)

Schizogyne sericea (L. fil.) DC.
Spanish common name: SALADO.

Schizogyne glaberrima DC.
Spanish common name: SALADO.

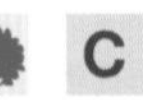

Schizogyne sericea.

This Canary endemic occurs on all the islands of the archipelago and is particularly widespread in coastal areas. A woody, densely branched shrub, it can reach a height of up to 1 metre and is characterised by its sericeous stems and its simple, greyish-white linear leaves that are up to 5 cm long. Its yellow flowers take the form of heads (capitula) that, bereft of ligules, feature a series of florets arranged in clusters measuring about 5 mm in diameter, which in turn are grouped into dense terminal inflorescences. A characteristic feature of its cypsela-style fruit is the presence of a scaly pappus with a row of simple hairs. There is another species belonging to this genus, namely *Schizogyne glaberrima* DC., which is exclusive to the island of Gran Canaria and can be distinguished from *Schizogyne sericea* by means of its shorter, filiform, green leaves and the pale-yellow colour of its flowers.

Schizogyne glaberrima.

HELIOTROPIUM RAMOSISSIMUM

Family
BORAGINACEAE (FORGET-ME-NOT)

Heliotropium ramosissimum (Lehm.) DC.
Spanish common name: CAMELLERA, HIERBA CAMELLA, VERRUQUERA.

Heliotropium ramosissimum.

Enjoying a wide distribution in Northern Africa and the Canary Islands, this species is quoted as being present throughout the archipelago, with the sole exception of the island of El Hierro. A creeping plant, it features alternate, simple leaves that are ovoidal-rhombic in shape, have a greyish hue and exhibit very prominent veins, particularly on the undersides of the leaves. Its small, white tubular flowers, which have 5 lobes and 5 stamens inserted on the corolla, are grouped into dense cymose inflorescences. The fruit of this plant is minute and has the appearance of small nuts. Being as it is a species principally associated with sandy substrata, *Heliotropium ramosissim*um reflects the processes of change or degradation affecting the original communities.

CAKILE MARITIMA

Family
BRASSICACEAE (MUSTARD)

Cakile maritima Scop.
Spanish common name: RÁBANO MARINO.

Cakile maritima.

Although on the Canary Islands this species is only to be found on Lanzarote and Fuerteventrua, it nevertheless enjoys a wide distribution along the coasts of the Mediterranean and the Atlantic, ranging from Morocco to Norway. An annual, rather succulent plant with stems that branch out from the base, it can reach a height of up to 40 cm. *Cakile maritima* has petiolate, succulent, lobed leaves, the lobes being variable in number (from 3 to 10) and ranging in shape from elliptic to spatulate. Its flowers are arranged into terminal racemes and each comprise 4 petals that are up to 1 cm long and generally white – though occasionally lilac – in colour. It fruit takes the form of capsules which, measuring up to 2 cm in length, are divided into two parts, the lower of which is smaller and features two lateral projections. Characteristic of sandy substrata, this plant has been used to combat scurvy.

GYMNOCARPOS DECANDER

Family
CARYOPHYLLACEAE (PINK)

CA

Gymnocarpos decander Forssk.

This species, which is not commonly found on the Canary Islands, has been reported to occur on the islands of Lanzarote, Fuerteventura, Gran Canaria and Tenerife. A small, highly ramified shrub, it features outstretched branches with very distinct knots. It has entire, subcylindrical, fleshy leaves that are greyish-green in colour. Measuring up to 2 cm in length, they are arranged in an opposite fashion or in fascicles on the stem. The flowers have no corolla and comprise 5 yellowish-green sepals above which 5 stamen are seen to project. These tiny flowers are grouped into small terminal inflorescences measuring less than 1 cm in diameter. The flowering period of *Gymnocarpos decander* spans the winter and spring months.

Gymnocarpos decander.

HERNIARIA FONTANESII

Family

CARYOPHYLLACEAE (PINK)

Herniaria fontanesii Gay.

Herniaria fontanesii.

The distribution of this small shrub encompasses Northern Africa and the Canary Archipelago, where it appears on the islands of Tenerife, Gran Canaria and Fuerteventura. A small-sized woody plant, it forms cushions standing up to 5 cm high. Its short leaves (less than 5 mm long) are oblong in shape, fleshy and greyish-green, whilst its small flowers (measuring under 2 mm) are arranged into whitish-green terminal racemes. The flowering period of *Herniaria fontanesii* spans the winter and spring months. This plant is a protected species listed in Annexe II of the Order issued by the Autonomous Community of the Canary Islands regarding the protection of wild flora.

POLYCARPAEA NIVEA

Family

CARYOPHYLLACEAE (PINK)

Polycarpaea nivea (Ait.) Webb.

Spanish common name: LENGUA DE PÁJARO.

Endemic to the Macaronesian floral region and Northern Africa, this taxon is to be found on all the islands of the archipelago with the exception of La Gomera. Highly variable in morphological terms, this is a short, woody, creeping plant featuring knotty stems. Its small leaves (under 2 cm) are rhomboidal in shape, fleshy and have a silvery hue. The tiny whitish-yellow flowers are grouped into small terminal inflorescences. *Polycarpaea nivea* is a species characteristic of the sandy substrata of the islands' coastlines, although it is also seen to thrive in rocky coastal areas.

Polycarpaea nivea.

CONVOLVULUS CAPUT-MEDUSAE

Family

CONVOLVULACEAE (BINDWEED)

Convolvulus caput-medusae Lowe.

Spanish common name: CHAPARRO.

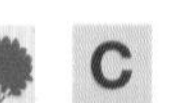

Convolvulus caput-medusae.

This most singular thorny shrub is only to be found on the islands of Gran Canaria and Fuerteventura, although it is closely related to other species belonging to the same genus occurring in Northern Africa. Having a stunted, globular appearance, it features abundant greyish-green branches that become thorny towards their ends. It has grey-hued, silky, spatulate leaves and pinkish-white, solitary, bell-shaped flowers measuring over 1 cm in diameter. The fruit it bears is small and purple. *Convolvulus caput-medusae* has a long flowering period that can last from January to August. It is a species characteristic of sandy substrata, although it can also grow on stony substrata and at ravine mouths. The survival of this species is seriously threatened by the destruction and disruption of its habitat, especially on Gran Canaria, and consequently it is protected both under Community legislation (classified as a Priority Species in keeping with the Habitats Directive) and that of the Autonomous Community of the Canary Islands (listed in Annexe I of the Flora Order).

CHENOLEOIDES TOMENTOSA

Family

CHENOPODIACEAE (GOOSEFOOT)

Chenoleoides tomentosa (Lowe) Botsch.

Spanish common name: SALADO LANUDO, ALGAHUERA.

Chenoleoides tomentosa.

Endemic to Northern Africa and Macaronesia, this species appears on all the islands except La Gomera. A shrub characteristic of sandy substrata, it can also grow in degraded areas. This is a perennial plant that normally takes the shape of a cushion and features up-swept branches that are more or less buried in the substratum. Its small, silver-grey leaves are entire, fleshy and cylindrical. Its tiny flowers are normally singly-borne or grouped together in small fascicles in the axils of the leaves.

SALSOLA MARUJAE

Family
CHENOPODIACEAE (GOOSEFOOT)

Salsola marujae Castroviejo et Luceño.
Spanish common name: BRUSCA, MATO.

Salsola marujae.

This singularly-named shrub is distributed all over the Macaronesian region and appears on all the islands of the Canary archipelago except El Hierro. A highly variable plant, it is densely branched and grows to a height of 1 metre. Its somewhat greyish-green leaves are linear and fleshy and are apparently arranged in whorls. *Salsola marujae* has tiny axillary flowers and one of its most distinctive features is the morphology of its fruit, which takes the form of very striking reddish-hued discs measuring up to 1 cm in diameter. It blooms from July to December.

SARCOCORNIA FRUTICOSA

Family
CHENOPODIACEAE (GOOSEFOOT)

Sarcocornia fruticosa (L.) A. J. Scott.
Spanish common name: MATO.

Sarcocornia fruticosa.

Belonging to a segregate genus of *Arthrocnemum,* this species is distributed in the easternmost islands of the Canary Archipelago, although it may well have already disappeared from Gran Canaria. A succulent shrub that can measure over a metre in diameter, it features greyish-green, up-turned, clearly articulated stems on which its very small leaves are arranged. *Sarcocornia fruticosa* has tiny yellowish-hued flowers that are situated in the leaf axils and its flowering period can last virtually all year round. Due to the resistance it displays in conditions of extreme salinity, it ranks as one of the most representative shrubs of coastal pools and saltmarshes, where it can grow as thick scrub. This species is protected by the legislation of the Autonomous Community of the Canaries (Annexe II of the Flora Order).

SUAEDA VERMICULATA

Family
CHENOPODIACEAE (GOOSEFOOT)

Suaeda vermiculata Forssk. ex J. F. Gmel.
Spanish common name: MATOMORO.

Suaeda vermiculata.

This species of Northern Africa and Macaronesia is found on Tenerife, Gran Canaria, Fuerteventura and Lanzarote. It is a densely branched shrub whose greyish-green, fleshy leaves are almost cylindrical and measure less than 5 mm in length. Its tiny, yellow-hued flowers are located in the axils of the leaves borne on the youngest branches. The plant blooms practically all year round. It is very common in areas of high salinity, where it forms dense thickets alongside other species of the same family.

TRAGANUM MOQUINII

Family
CHENOPODIACEAE (GOOSEFOOT)

Traganum moquinii Webb ex Moq. In DC.
Spanish common name: BALANCÓN.

Traganum moquinii.

Native to the Saharan coast, this shrub also occurs on the Canary Archipelago, where it appears on the eastern islands as well as on Tenerife and La Gomera. A densely branched perennial, it can grow to a height of over a metre and a half. It features greyish-green, succulent leaves that are almost triangular in shape and measure up to 1 cm long. The tiny yellow flowers of this plant, which blooms practically all year round, are located in the axils of the leaves. This species is characteristic of the Canary archipelago dune systems, above all those on Gran Canaria and Fuerteventura, where it forms fairly widespread monospecific scrub. Its status as one of the archipelago's protected species is founded on its inclusion in Annexe II of the Autonomous Community's Order concerning the conservation of wild flora.

EUPHORBIA APHYLLA

Family
EUPHORBIACEAE (SPURGE)

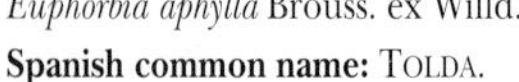

Euphorbia aphylla Brouss. ex Willd.
Spanish common name: TOLDA.

  C

Euphorbia aphylla.

This most singular Canary endemic occurs on the islands of La Gomera, Tenerife and Gran Canaria, its existence also having been reported on Fuerteventura. It has a shrubby stature and can grow to a height of over 80 cm. The stem is woody at its base, but displays younger sections that are green and fleshy. The distinguishing feature of this species is the absence of leaves, its flowers being arranged terminally on the young branches. The flowers are small and have a yellowish hue, whereas its fruit is borne in the form of reddish three-valved capsules. *Euphorbia aphylla* blooms in the late spring and early summer months. All parts of this plant contain a poisonous, whitish latex. It is a species characteristic of rocky coastal substrata, above all those of the northern shores of the islands. Enjoying protection under the provisions of Autonomous Community legislation (Annexe II of the Flora Order), it is becoming an increasingly common sight in gardens.

EUPHORBIA PARALIAS

Family

EUPHORBIACEAE (SPURGE)

Euphorbia paralias L.

Spanish common name: LECHERUELA.

Widely distributed in the Atlantic and Mediterranean regions, this curious species is to be found on the eastern Canary Islands, as well as on Tenerife and La Gomera. It features erect, rather fleshy, stiff stems and, branching out at its base, reaches a height of 50 cm. Its glaucous, greenish-hued, rather fleshy leaves are lanceolate in shape and reach a length of up to 3 cm. The orange-green flowers of this plant are grouped into more or less dense terminal inflorescences. Its fruit is borne in the form of small, brownish capsules. *Euphorbia paralias* blooms in summer and autumn. Despite being a species typical of sandy systems, it can also grow in degraded environments.

Euphorbia paralias.

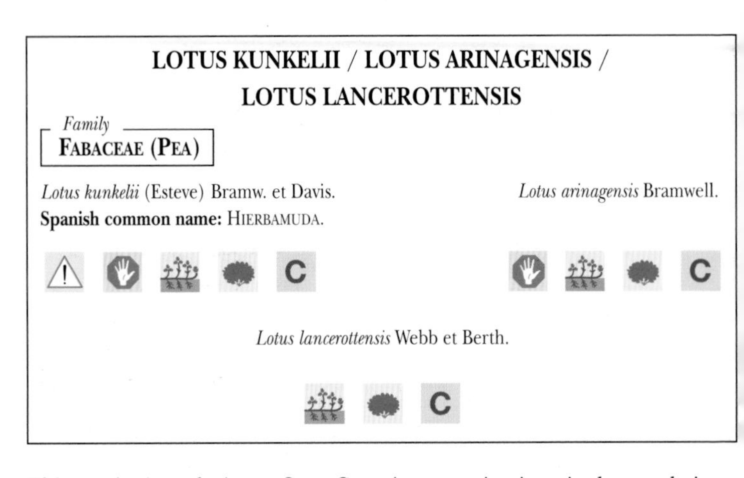

LOTUS KUNKELII / LOTUS ARINAGENSIS / LOTUS LANCEROTTENSIS

Family
FABACEAE (PEA)

Lotus kunkelii (Esteve) Bramw. et Davis.
Spanish common name: HIERBAMUDA.

C

Lotus arinagensis Bramwell.

C

Lotus lancerottensis Webb et Berth.

C

This species is exclusive to Gran Canaria, occurring in a single population on the island's eastern coast. A woody, pseudo-creeping plant, it forms subshrub-like cushions standing up to 30 cm high. It features green stems with sessile tri-or quinquefoliolate leaves arranged in whorls. Measuring up to 1 cm long, the leaflets are obovate in shape, fleshy, and are clothed in a clearly visible layer of thin hair. Its yellow flowers appear in groups of 3 or 4

Lotus lancerottensis.

Lotus kunkelii.

on long peduncles arising from the terminal section of the branches. The fruit borne by this plant take the form of straight pods that are 2 to 3.5 cm long and contain up to 12 seeds. This species is characteristic of the sandy systems of the eastern coast of Gran Canaria and is probably one of the species in greatest danger of extinction in all the archipelago, owing to the drastic reduction in its numbers and the destruction of its natural habitat. Consequently, its conservation is addressed in all the prevailing legislation concerning the protection of the flora of the Canary Islands (*Lotus kunkelii* is listed in Annexe I of the Berne Agreement; it is classified as a Priority Species under the EC Habitats Directive; it ranks as a species "in danger of extinction" in the National Catalogue of Endangered Species; and is regarded as a species meriting strict protection within the Autonomous Community of the Canary Islands). Closely related to this species are those of *Lotus arinagensis* Bramwell, whose distribution is restricted to the sandy habitats of the eastern coast of Gran Canaria; and *Lotus lancerottensis* Webb et Berth., which itself is exclusive to the islands of Fuerteventura and Lanzarote.

Lotus arinagensis.

LOTUS MACULATUS

Family

FABACEAE (PEA)

Lotus maculatus Breitf.

Spanish common name: PICO DE PALOMA.

C

Lotus maculatus.

This beautiful Canary endemic is exclusive to the northern coast of the island of Tenerife, where at present it is represented by no more than two populations. A procumbent, subshrub-like plant, it features long, flexible branches that can grow to over 1 metre in length. Its leaves are long, green and linear-oblanceolate. Its axillary inflorescences are grouped into fascicles of 2 to 4 yellow flowers, each of which has one petal that takes the form of a reddish carina. The seeds of this plant are contained in brown pods up to 3 cm long. Generally speaking, the flowering period of *Lotus maculatus* spans the months of February and August. Even though this species is used extensively in the gardens of the Canary Islands on account of its spectacular blooms and its potential as a carpeting plant, its natural populations display a scarcity of specimens and consequently it is subject to strict protection measures *(Lotus maculatus* is listed in Annexe I of the Berne Agreement; it is classified as a species "in danger of extinction" in the National Catalogue of Endangered Species; and appears in Annexe II of the Flora Order).

ONONIS NATRIX

Family
FABACEAE (PEA)

Ononis natrix L.

Spanish common name: GATUÑA, MELOJA.

Ononis natrix.

Native to the western Mediterranean, this species also occurs on the Canary archipelago. Despite being a very common sight on Fuerteventura, Lanzarote and La Graciosa, it is much less widely distributed on Gran Canaria and Tenerife. A densely branched shrub featuring viscous, sticky leaves, it grows to a height of up to a metre and a half. The posterior edges of its yellow flowers boast a very striking reddish hue. *Ononis natrix* has short pods containing a small amount of seeds. It is a characteristic element of the islands' coastal dunes and sandy expanses.

FRANKENIA LAEVIS

Family
FRANKENIACEAE (ALKALI-HEATH)

Frankenia laevis L.
Spanish common name: TOMILLO, SAPERA, ALBOHOL.

Frankenia laevis.

This very widely distributed species occurs on all the islands of the archipelago. A densely branched, procumbent, subshrub-like plant, it forms cushions that reach a height of no more than 25 cm. Its leaves are short, linear, simple and revolute. The relatively small, whitish-pink flowers are arranged in terminal racemes, which make the plant a spectacle of colour when in bloom. *Frankenia laevis* is part of the habitual floristic ensemble gracing the plant communities of the islands' coastal areas.

LIMONIUM PAPILLATUM

Family
PLUMBAGINACEAE (THRIFT)

Limonium papillatum (Webb et Berth.). O. Kuntze.
Spanish common name: SIEMPREVIVA (SEMPERVIVUM).

This Canary endemic belonging to the thrift family is restricted to the islands of Fuerteventura, Lanzarote and the eastern islets. A small-proportioned, relatively short plant, it has characteristic zigzagging stems. Its leaves are spatulate and rather fleshy. Adding to the colour provided by its small flowers are the large pinkish-white bracts. *Limonium papillatum* enjoys protection under the legislation of the Canary Islands (it is listed in Annexe II of the Flora Order).

Limonium papillatum.

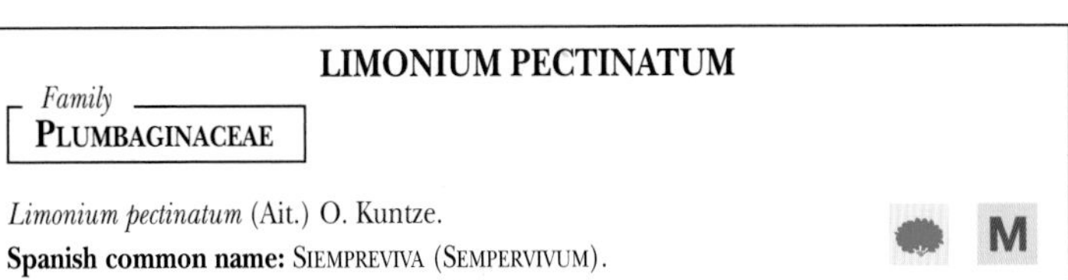

LIMONIUM PECTINATUM

Family
PLUMBAGINACEAE

Limonium pectinatum (Ait.) O. Kuntze.
Spanish common name: SIEMPREVIVA (SEMPERVIVUM).

M

This sempervivum appears in the coastal areas of each of the Canary Islands, its distribution likewise encompassing other archipelagos of the Macaronesian floral region. At least 4 varieties have been described for this small shrub, which displays a wide variety of sizes and morphological features. Generally speaking, it has rosette-shaped, spatulate leaves that can grow to a length of up to 4 cm. Appearing only on the upper sections of the branches, the pinkish-hued flowers of *Limonium pectinatum* are grouped into tightly-packed inflorescences.

Limonium pectinatum.

RESEDA SCOPARIA

Family

RESEDACEAE (MIGNONETTE)

Reseda scoparia Brouss. ex Willd.

Spanish common name: GUALDA.

Occurring on the islands of La Palma, La Gomera, Tenerife and Gran Canaria, this subshrub-like plant stands less than 50 cm tall and features flexible terminal branches. It has greyish-green, linear, fleshy leaves and small, greenish-white flowers with prominent stamens. Perhaps the most characteristic aspect of this species is its fruit, which takes the form of highly conspicuous tubular green capsules. *Reseda scoparia* blooms from January to May. It, too, is subject to strict protection measures within the Autonomous Community of the Canary Islands (listed in Annexe II of the Flora Order).

Reseda scoparia.

KUNKELIELLA SUBSUCCULENTA

Family

SANTALACEAE (SANDALWOOD)

Kunkeliella subsucculenta Kämmer.

Spanish common name: ESCOBILLA.

Kunkeliella subsucculenta.

This rare semiparasitic shrub is found at a single location on the northern coast of Tenerife. A densely branched plant of variable height, it features succulent green stems. Its small, scaly leaves are under 1.5 mm long, whilst its flowers are arranged singly and apically on the stems. Measuring less than 2.5 mm, these small sessile flowers are greenish-white in colour and have 5 petals. Its fruit takes the form of small, fleshy drupes. In light of its current state of conservation, *Kunkeliella subsucculenta* ranks as an endangered species and is listed in Annexe I of the Berne Agreement, Annexe II of the Habitats Directive and Annexe I of the Flora Order.

KICKXIA SAGITTATA VAR. URBANII

Family
SCROPHULARIACEAE (FOXGLOVE)

Kickxia sagittata var. *urbanii* (Pit.) Sund.

This curious variety belonging to the foxglove family is endemic to the Canary Islands, where it is found on Tenerife, Gran Canaria, Fuerteventura and Lanzarote. A densely branched, green-stemmed, perennial, procumbent plant, it has a compact, cushion-like appearance. Its rather fleshy, greenish-hued leaves range in shape from linear to oblong and taper towards their base. *Kickxia sagittata* bears highly characteristic yellow flowers, each of which displays one spur-like petal that is slightly curved at its end. Its fruit appears in the form of ovoidal capsules.

Kickxia sagittata.

LYCIUM INTRICATUM

Family
SOLANACEAE (POTATO)

Lycium intricatum Boiss.

Spanish common name: ESPINO, ESPINO DE MAR.

Lycium intricatum.

This species occurs on the Canary Islands, in Northern Africa and in some areas of Southern Europe. It has been reported throughout the archipelago with the exception of the island of El Hierro. A thorny shrub having a high ecological valence, this plant displays a certain ruderal-nitrophilous nature and is typical of regressive stages of climax plant communities in the low-lying areas of the islands. Its leaves are small, greyish-green and fleshy, whereas its flowers, which are arranged singly on the stems, feature a violet hue and are tubular in shape. The fruit borne by *Lycium intricatum* is brilliant red in colour.

TAMARIX CANARIENSIS

Family

TAMARICACEAE (TAMARISK)

Tamarix canariensis Willd.

Spanish common name: TARAJAL (CANARY TAMARISK).

Tamarix canariensis.

Occurring on all the islands of the archipelago except El Hierro, this shrub can grow to heights of over a metre. The bark of its stem has a characteristic reddish-brown hue, whilst its leaves are small (measuring 1 to 3 mm), scale-like, greyish-green and are arranged alternately on the branches. Its pinkish, pedicellate flowers are clustered into thin spikes on the young shoots. In certain areas of the archipelago this species is seen to form small thickets in sandy coastal environments and at ravine mouths. Its wood has been used both in the building of rivercraft and as a material for crop-protecting windbreaks. Commonly used in gardening, it is also renowned in popular medicine for its astringent properties. *Tamarix canariensis* is protected under regional legislation (it is listed in Annexe II of the Flora Order).

ZYGOPHYLLUM FONTANESII

Family

ZYGOPHYLLACEAE (BEAN CAPER, CREOSOTE BUSH)

Zygophyllum fontanesii Webb et Berth.

Spanish common name: UVILLA DE MAR.

Typically found in the sandy substrata and rocky environments of coastal areas, this species is endemic to the Macaronesian region and Northern Africa, occurring throughout the archipelago with the exception of the island of La Palma. A shrub reaching heights of up to 50 cm, it features woody, articulate, slightly brownish-grey-hued stems. Its cylindrical, fleshy leaves are green when young and turn a yellowish colour before falling. The pinkish flowers it bears are hardly noticeable, unlike its fleshy, orange-coloured fruit, which is spherical in shape and measures over 5 mm in diameter. *Zygophyllum fontanesii* is protected under regional legislation (it is listed in Annexe II of the Flora Order).

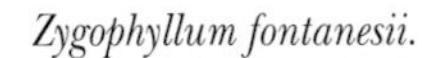

Zygophyllum fontanesii.

CYPERUS CAPITATUS

Family
CYPERACEAE (SEDGE)

Cyperus capitatus Vand.

Cyperus capitatus.

A widely distributed species that on the Canary archipelago is to be found on the islands of Tenerife, Gran Canaria, Fuerteventura and Lanzarote. A characteristic feature of this plant are its creeping rhizomes, from which the stems arise, bearing the inflorescences at their apices. *Cyperus capitatus* is typical of sandy coastal areas, above all those of Lanzarote and Fuerteventura.

Basal-layer Communities

The climax communities of the basal layer are seen to basically consist of variable-cover scrub, which comprises species that have developed a great number of adaptive strategies (such as succulence, leaf loss, leaf-surface reduction, production of hair) in order to survive in the adverse conditions prevailing in their habitat. Indeed, these communities are subjected to considerable hydric stress owing to their location in areas recording annual precipitation figures of less than 300 mm, areas that display a soil water deficit practically all year round. Basal-layer communities likewise have to endure considerable thermal stress and high insolation levels.

The most representative communities of this layer or altitudinal zone are the spurge formations called "tabaibales" *(Euphorbia balsamifera)* and "cardonales" *(Euphorbia canariensis)*. Extending all over the lower-lying areas of the islands, the *tabaibales* are not normally to be found at altitudes of over 400 m in the northern areas, whereas on the southern slopes they can be seen above 800 m. Although the *cardonales* enjoy a somewhat similar distribution, they generally occur in areas marked by greater soil shortage and more adverse edaphic conditions. Worthy of special mention here are the spurge formations whose predominant species is the "tolda" *(Euphorbia aphylla)*. These particular *tabaibales* are widespread in the northern sections of the islands of La Gomera, Tenerife and Gran Canaria.

Furthermore, these communities are accompanied by a large number of other species, of which we should highlight the white viper's bugloss or "tajinaste blanco" *(Echium decaisnei)*, the "verode" *(Kleinia neriifolia)*, the "cardoncillo" *(Ceropegia* sp.), the "balo" *(Plocama pendula)*, the "cornical" *(Periploca laevigata)*, the "tasaigo" *(Rubia fruticosa)*, and several Asparagus species.

The degradation series of these communities consist of replacement scrub, which at present enjoys a wide distribution and whose predominant species are the spurge called "tabaiba morisca" *(Euphorbia regis-jubae)*, "aulaga" *(Launaea arborescens)*, "leña buena" *(Neochamaelea pulverulenta)*, "balo" *(Plocama pendula)* and grass communities.

CARALLUMA BURCHARDII

Family
ASCLEPIADACEAE (MILKWEED)

Caralluma burchardii N.E. Br.
Spanish common name: CUERNÚA.

This curious species is only to be found on the islands of Fuerteventura and Lanzarote. A succulent plant, it grows to a height of no more than 20 cm. It is characterised by its up-turned, quadrangular-sectioned, greyish-brown stems, the absence of leaves and its yellowish flowers that appear in terminal clusters on the stems. Its fruit takes the form of two horn-shaped follicles measuring approximately 10 cm. An endangered species, *Caralluma burchardii* is protected under prevailing legislation (it is listed in Annexe I of the Berne Agreement; Annexe II of the EC Habitats Directive; and Annexe II of the Flora Order).

Caralluma burchardii.

CEROPEGIA DICHOTOMA

Family
ASCLEPIADACEAE (MILKWEED)

Ceropegia dichotoma Haw.
Spanish common name: CARDONCILLO.

Ceropegia dichotoma.

his Canary endemic, which occurs on the islands of La Palma, El Hierro, a Gomera and Tenerife, belongs to a taxonomically rather complex group, or which a total of 4 different species have been described, namely *Ceropegia ians* for the island of La Palma, *C. chrysantha* for Tenerife, *C. krainzii* and *. cerathophora.* Other authors limit the number of species to just one, amely *C. dichotoma,* although they do recognise the existence of two ubspecies. The characteristic feature of this plant is its up-turned, succulent, ircular-sectioned olive-green stems. Its inflorescences comprise a small umber of pale-yellow, tubular flowers over 3 cm long, whilst its horn-shaped uit features two follicles measuring 12 cm. *Ceropegia dichotoma* is protected nder regional legislation (it is listed in Annexe II of the Flora Order).

CEROPEGIA FUSCA

Family
ASCLEPIADACEAE (MILKWEED)

Ceropegia fusca Bolle.
Spanish common name: CARDONCILLO.

C

Ceropegia fusca.

A succulent Canary endemic that is described as existing on the islands of La Palma, Tenerife and Gran Canaria. Branched from its base, this plant features erect, cylindrical, articulate, greyish (occasionally greenish) stems that can reach a height of over a metre and a half. It is a deciduous species whose linear, opposite leaves measure up to 5 cm long. Its highly characteristic flowers are clustered together in small groups of 2 to 5 at the stem axils. Tubular in shape, they are reddish-brown and feature lobes that are joined at the tips when young. The fruit borne by this plant is capsular and comprises two follicles over 10 cm long. *Ceropegia fusca* blooms in the spring and summer months. A common sight in the parks and gardens of the islands, it is protected under regional legislation (species listed in Annexe II of the Flora Order).

PERIPLOCA LAEVIGATA

Family
ASCLEPIADACEAE (MILKWEED)

Periploca laevigata Ait.
Spanish common name: CORNICAL.

Endemic to the Canary Islands and to Africa, this taxon occurs throughout the archipelago. A shrubby species featuring knotty, flexible stems, its behaviour is very often reminiscent of a climbing plant. It has oblanceolate leaves which, measuring over 5 cm long, are arranged oppositely at each knot of the stem. Its terminal cyme inflorescences comprise a relatively small number of flowers characterised by their star-like shape and their singular colouring - reddish on the inside, green on the outside. In the same manner as the previous species, the fruit borne by *Periploca laevigata* consists of two brown follicles measuring up to 12 cm long. This plant is characteristic of the spurge communities *(cardonal-tabaibal)* occurring in the low-lying areas of the islands.

Periploca laevigata.

ARGYRANTHEMUM FOENICULACEUM

Family
ASTERACEAE (DAISY)

Argyranthemum foeniculaceum (Willd.) Webb ex Sch. Bip.
Spanish common name: MAGARZA.

C

Argyranthemum foeniculaceum.

This highly beautiful shrub-like daisy is only to be found on the island of Tenerife, where it occurs frequently at altitudes of between 200 and 1,800 metres. Reaching a height of up to 1 metre, it has a characteristic candelabra-like appearance. Its divided leaves (bi- or tripinnatisect) are a glaucous-green colour and feature linear lobes. The flower heads of *Argyranthemum foeniculaceum,* complete with white ligules, are arranged singly (rarely being clustered) and have a diameter of over 2 cm. This species is protected under regional legislation by means of the Flora Order (Annexe II).

ARGYRANTHEMUM LIDII

Family
ASTERACEAE (DAISY)

Argyranthemum lidii Humphr.

Argyranthemum lidii.

This rare, singular species endemic to Gran Canaria has but a few populations, located amidst the craggy landscape of the north-western section of the island. A subshrub-like plant, it features ascending branches measuring up to 60 cm, divided, bipinnatisect, ovate-elliptic, glabrous leaves up to 9 cm long. Its inflorescences comprise a small number of flower heads, which display brown peduncles and white ligules. *Argyranthemum lidii* has a flowering period that spans the months of March and April. This is a rare, extremely local species considered to be in danger of extinction. Consequently, it is subject to strict protection measures (it is listed in Annexe I of the Berne Agreement; classified as a Priority Species under the EC Habitats Directive; considered a species "in danger of extinction" in the National Catalogue of Endangered Species; and regarded as a species meriting strict protection under the regional Flora Order).

ARGYRANTHEMUM MADERENSE

Family
ASTERACEAE (DAISY)

Argyranthemum maderense (D. Don.) Humphr.
Spanish common name: MARGARITA, FLOR DE SANTA MARÍA (DAISY).

Argyranthemum maderense.

This Canary endemic occurs only on the island of Lanzarote, where it is quite rare. A branched shrub standing over 50 cm tall, its pinnatifid, spatulate leaves are glabrous and green in colour. The inflorescences feature short peduncles and a limited number of heads, whose major characteristic is the yellow hue of its ligules, a very uncommon feature for this genus. *Argyranthemum maderense* blooms from January to May. A highly ornamental plant, it is often used in the local parks and gardens. This species is protected under regional legislation by means of the Flora Order (Annexe II).

ATALANTHUS PINNATUS

Family
ASTERACEAE (DAISY)

Atalanthus pinnatus (L. fil.) D. Don.
Spanish common name: BALILLO.

Atalanthus pinnatus.

The distribution of this taxonomically rather complex shrub is restricted to the islands of Tenerife, Gran Canaria and Fuerteventura. Growing to a height of over a metre, it is a branched plant whose leaves are arranged terminally. It has split leaves featuring very fine, flat, linear lobes. Situated at the ends of the branches, its more or less dense inflorescences comprise small heads (under 3 mm in diameter) and yellow ligules. *Atalanthus pinnatus* is a species characteristic of the rocky environments, escarpments and rock walls of the xeric zones of the archipelago.

HELICHRYSUM GOSSYPINUM

Family
ASTERACEAE (DAISY)

Helichrysum gossypinum Webb.
Spanish common name: YESQUERA, ALGODONERA.

Helichrysum gossypinum.

This singular endemic species is exclusive to Lanzarote, being a common sight in the northern area of the island. A very hairy, white perennial rock plant, it reaches a height of up to 30 cm. Its leaves are soft, oblanceolate and sericeous, whilst its flowers are arranged in tightly-packed inflorescences featuring yellowish-hued heads (capitula). *Helichrysum gossypinum* blooms from April to June and its use is becoming increasingly popular in local parks and gardens on account of its great ornamental value. Regarded as a vulnerable species, it is listed in Annexe I of the Berne Agreement, in Annexe II of the EC Habitats Directive, and is classified as a strictly protected species under regional legislation (Annexe I of the Flora Order).

KLEINIA NERIIFOLIA

Family
ASTERACEAE (DAISY)

Kleinia neriifolia Haw.
Spanish common name: VEROL, VERODE.

Kleinia neriifolia.

This widespread thick-stemmed plant occurs on all the islands of the archipelago. It is a branched, succulent, shrubby species with cylindrical, fleshy, greyish-green stems that are covered with the scars left by fallen leaves. Its rather fleshy, lance-shaped, green leaves are located at the ends of the branches and can be up to 12 cm long. *Kleinia neriifolia* has a tightly-packed inflorescence comprising numerous yellowish flowers. Its fruits feature very striking feathery pappi. This species has a long flowering period spanning the months of summer and autumn.

LAUNAEA ARBORESCENS

Family
ASTERACEAE (DAISY)

Launaea arborescens (Batt.) Murb.
Spanish common name: AULAGA.

Typical of arid areas, this species occurs all over the Canary Islands, as well as in Northern Africa and Southern Europe. A densely branched shrub, its stems have acquired a thorny appearance. Its leaves – which only appear in juvenile specimens or during the winter months – vary greatly in both shape and size and have a somewhat fleshy consistency. Measuring over 1 cm in diameter, the plant's yellow flowers are arranged singly at the ends of its branches. *Launaea arborescens* blooms in the spring and summer months. It is a species characteristic of the hot, dry areas in which the islands' lowland climax communities have undergone a certain degree of degradation.

Launaea arborescens.

NAUPLIUS SCHULTZII

Family
ASTERACEAE (DAISY)

Nauplius schultzii (Bolle) Wikl.

Nauplius schultzii.

This very brightly coloured shrub is only to be found on the islands of Fuerteventura and Lanzarote. Characteristically a short, small-proportioned plant, it forms small, tightly-packed cushions. It has spatulate, hairy, rather fleshy leaves with dentate margins. Measuring no more than 3 cm in diameter, its flower heads are arranged singly and feature yellowish-white ligules. *Nauplius schultzii* is one of the Canary Islands' protected species and is listed in Annexe II of the Flora Order.

NAUPLIUS SERICEUS / NAUPLIUS INTERMEDIUS

Family
ASTERACEAE (DAISY)

Nauplius sericeus (L. fil.) Cass.
Spanish common name: JORAO.

  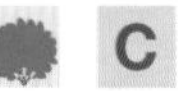

Nauplius intermedius Webb in Webb et Berth.

A brightly coloured shrub only to be found on the island of Fuerteventura, where it is locally quite abundant. Growing nearly a metre tall, this is a densely branched plant whose old stems are a blackish-grey colour. Its oblanceolate leaves, which measure 3 to 5 cm long and have a silver hue on both sides, are generally located at the ends of the branches. The bright yellow flower heads (capitula) are over 5 cm in diameter and are singly arranged at the apices of the stems. This shrub is very commonly used in the parks and gardens of the islands. Closely related to this species is *Nauplius intermedius* Webb in Webb et Berth., a taxon that is endemic to the island of Lanzarote and which can be distinguished from *Nauplius sericeus* by its silver stems and its smaller-sized leaves.

Nauplius sericeus.

Nauplius intermedius.

ECHIUM DECAISNEI

Family
BORAGINACEAE (FORGET-ME-NOT)

Echium decaisnei Webb.
Spanish common name: TAJINASTE BLANCO (WHITE VIPER'S BUGLOSS).

C

Echium decaisnei.

This Canary endemic occurs on the islands of Gran Canaria, Fuerteventura and Lanzarote, the last two of which also feature the subspecies *purpuriense.* A densely branched woody shrub, it can grow to a height of 2 metres. A characteristic feature of this plant is its lanceolate leaves covered in small spines that on the upper leaf surface are evenly distributed but which, on the underside of the leaf, are found only on the midrib and the margins. The white flowers borne by *Echium decaisnei* are grouped into tightly-packed conical inflorescences at the ends of the branches. Of great ornamental value, this species is a common sight in the parks and gardens of the islands. Enjoying protection under regional legislation, it is listed in Annexe II of the Flora Order.

HELIANTHEMUM CANARIENSE

Family

CISTACEAE (ROCKROSE)

Helianthemum canariense (Jacq.) Pers.

Spanish common name: TURMERO, RAMA CRÍA, JARILLA.

Helianthemum canariense.

This small shrub is to be found both in Northern Africa and on all the islands of the Canary archipelago. A stunted, woody, subshrub-like plant that stands no more than 20 cm tall, it is densely branched, as a result of which it has a rather tangled appearance. It features small, entire, ovate leaves that are a silver-grey colour. Its singly arranged pale yellow flowers measure less than 2 cm across and are not very consistent. This species is characteristic of the regeneration phases of sweet spurge formations.

NEOCHAMAELEA PULVERULENTA

Family
CNEORACEAE (SPURGE OLIVE)

Neochamaelea pulverulenta (Vent.) Erdtm.
Spanish common name: LEÑA BUENA, LEÑA SANTA, ORIJAMA.

C

Neochamaelea pulverulenta.

Regarded as sacred by the pre-Hispanic inhabitants of the islands, this species occurs throughout the archipelago, with the exception of Fuerteventura and Lanzarote. It is a densely branched shrub whose youngest shoots are covered with a silver layer of hair or tomentum. It features small, simple, almost linear, silver-grey leaves arranged alternately on the stems. Its yellow flowers grow singly on the petioles of the youngest leaves during the months of winter and spring. *Neochamaelea pulverulenta* bears a highly conspicuous, usually three-lobed, reddish-colour fruit. It was used extensively by the native peoples of the Canary Islands and has often been found in their graves. A plant of considerable medicinal value, it is renowned for its antiseptic and anticatarrhal properties. It has traditionally been taken as an infusion made basically using the stems. This species enjoys protection under the Order issued by the Autonomous Community of the Canary Islands regarding wild flora (Annexe II).

EUPHORBIA ATROPURPUREA

Family
EUPHORBIACEAE (SPURGE)

Euphorbia atropurpurea (Brouss.) Webb et Berth.
Spanish common name: TABAIBA ROJA (RED SPURGE).

Exclusive to the island of Tenerife, this Canary endemic is a plant of great beauty, especially when in bloom. It is a densely branched, succulent shrub that can grow up to 2 metres high. Clearly visible on its brown branches are the scars left by fallen leaves. It has large, greyish-green leaves that often feature purple blotches at their centre. Spatulate in shape, they are grouped into rosettes at the terminal sections of the branches. Rising above the leaves is a dense inflorescence comprising the purple-coloured flowers and bracts so characteristic of the species. The flowers bloom during the winter and spring months, giving rise to very conspicuous purple fruits. *Euphorbia atropurpurea* produces a sticky white, caustic latex. It is a species typical of the xeric environments occurring in the medium-altitude areas of southern Tenerife. A highly ornamental plant, it enjoys protection on a regional scale, being listed in Annexe II of the Flora Order.

Euphorbia atropurpurea.

EUPHORBIA BALSAMIFERA

Family
EUPHORBIACEAE (SPURGE)

Euphorbia balsamifera (Ait.).
Spanish common name: TABAIBA DULCE (SWEET SPURGE).

Euphorbia balsamifera.

Declared the official natural plant symbol of the island of Lanzarote by virtue of Regional Act 7/1991 dated 30th April, this spurge is to be found throughout the archipelago and also in Northern Africa. A woody, succulent shrub with knotty stems, it develops a globular appearance. It is variable in size, specimens ranging in height from only a few centimetres to over 3 metres, the latter figure being recorded on the island of Gran Canaria. It features small, fleshy, greenish leaves that are clustered together at the ends of the branches. Its small, yellowish-green flowers grow singly at the centre of the leaves. *Euphorbia balsamifera* has a long flowering period that can last from autumn right through to spring. Its fruit is globular in shape with three distinct reddish-coloured grooves. All parts of the plant contain a white, sticky, non-poisonous latex which, once dried, has traditionally been used as chewing gum and as a means of removing cysts and warts. Being of a certain ornamental value, this species of spurge is a common sight in the gardens of the islands.

EUPHORBIA CANARIENSIS

Family
EUPHORBIACEAE (SPURGE)

Euphorbia canariensis L.
Spanish common name: CARDÓN (CANARY SPURGE).

Euphorbia canariensis.

This Canary endemic occurs on all the islands of the archipelago. Somewhat cactus-like in appearance, it is a succulent, candelabra-shaped shrub that is capable of occupying large areas. It has erect, yellowish to greyish green branches that measure up to 3 metres high and are usually quadrangular in section. Clearly visible on the stems are the different segments corresponding to annual growth periods. The vertices of the stems feature short, slightly upwardly curving spines. In contrast to the plant's rather unspectacular reddish flowers, which develop at the apex of the branches, are its fruits which, taking the form of bright red trivalved capsules, are tightly packed into the ribs of the branches. *Euphorbia canariensis* blooms during the months of spring and summer. The latex produced by this shrub is poisonous. It is a species characteristic of the low-altitude landscape of the Canaries, above all those areas displaying greatest soil shortage and which act as a refuge for a large number of species such as the "cornical" *(Periploca laevigata)*, "tasaigo" *(Rubia fruticosa)*, "tabaiba" *(Spurges)* and "guaydil" *(Convolvulus floridus)*. Widely employed in local parks and gardens, it is protected under regional legislation (Annexe II, Flora Order). It was declared the official natural plant symbol of the island of Gran Canaria by virtue of Regional Act 7/1991 dated 30th April.

EUPHORBIA HANDIENSIS

Family
EUPHORBIACEAE (SPURGE)

Euphorbia handiensis Burch.
Spanish common name: CARDÓN DE JANDÍA (JANDÍA SPURGE).

As its common name would suggest, this cactus-shaped species is exclusive to the southern region of the island of Fuerteventura. A succulent plant measuring less than a metre in height, it features erect, thick, almost circular-sectioned stems with very clear venation, the number of ribs varying from 8 to 14. It has long, paired spines measuring over 2 cm. Its small, reddish-green flowers are less visible than its fruit, which takes the shape of reddish-brown capsules. Owing to the disturbance of its habitat and to indiscriminate picking for ornamental purposes, this species is on the verge of extinction and therefore is subject to strict protection measures (Annexe I of the Berne Agreement; Priority Species, EC Habitats Directive; Protected Species, Annexe II, Flora Order). It was declared the official natural plant symbol of the island of Fuerteventura by virtue of Regional Act 7/1991 dated 30th April.

Euphorbia handiensis.

EUPHORBIA REGIS-JUBAE

Family
EUPHORBIACEAE (SPURGE)

Euphorbia regis-jubae Webb et Berth.
Spanish common name: TABAIBA AMARGA, TABAIBA MORA.

Euphorbia regis-jubae.

Characteristic of the easternmost Canary Islands (Gran Canaria, Fuerteventura and Lanzarote), this spurge also occurs in Northern Africa. A succulent shrub growing to a height of 2 metres, this species is not branched from its base and features a light brown stem. Its narrowly oblong, pale green leaves are arranged alternately at the ends of the branches, whilst the small greenish-hued flowers are loosely clustered in terminal inflorescences, the highlight of which is the larger, greenish-yellow bracts. *Euphorbia regis-jubae* bears a small, reddish-coloured fruit. Despite being typically found in the low-lying areas of the archipelago, as a result of its great adaptability this species is readily found at altitudes of over 1,000 metres.

SALVIA CANARIENSIS

Family
LAMIACEAE (MINT)

Salvia canariensis L.
Spanish common name: SALVIA, SALVIA MORISCA, GARITOPA.

Salvia canariensis.

This widely distributed Canary endemic occurs on all the islands of the archipelago. The Canary sage is a shrub that can grow up to 2 metres high and whose long branches feature a dense arrangement. Its large, lanceolate leaves are basally sagittate and measure over 12 cm long, whilst its more or less dense inflorescences comprise violet-coloured flowers. Employed for a variety of medicinal purposes, this plant is renowned for its antipyretic properties and is recommended for stomach complaints, diabetes, etc. The use of *Salvia canariensis* is regulated by the provisions of the Flora Order regarding the species listed in its Annexe III.

TEUCRIUM HETEROPHYLLUM

Family
LAMIACEAE (MINT)

Teucrium heterophyllum L'Hér.
Spanish common name: JOCAMA.

Teucrium heterophyllum.

This singularly beautiful Macaronesian endemic occurs on the islands of La Palma, La Gomera, Tenerife and Gran Canaria. A shrub reaching a height of up to 2 metres, it features fragile stems, the youngest shoots being covered with a tomentum endowing them with a silky appearance. Its simple, lanceolate to ovate leaves are a greenish colour above and thickly hairy underneath. *Teucrium heterophyllum* has spectacular orange-red flowers arranged in small clusters of 1 to 4. These are bilabiate flowers boasting short, bilobed upper lips and larger, trilobed lower lips. A characteristic feature of this species is its unusually long stamens and styles, which soar to twice the length of the corolla. Having a certain ornamental value, it can be found in some of the parks and gardens of the archipelago.

RUMEX LUNARIA

Family
POLYGONACEAE (DOCK)

Rumex lunaria L.
Spanish common name: VINAGRERA, CALCOSA.

This Canary endemic occurs throughout the archipelago. Densely branched from its base, it is an evergreen shrub that reaches heights of over a metre. It has fragile, knotty, reddish-coloured stems, whilst its simple, petiolate, bright green leaves are cordate and rather fleshy. The leaves are arranged alternately on the stems, whose apices bear racemose inflorescences comprising small greenish flowers. *Rumex lunaria* features dry, reddish-hued fruits that like the flowers are arranged in spectacular racemes. This species is commonly found in rather degraded environments such as abandoned arable land, roadside areas and stony expanses, where it plays an important role as the *primocoloniser* or first species to become established. Having been used as a fodder plant, it also serves a number of medicinal purposes. The juice obtained by crushing the leaves helps to unblock the nasal cavity, whilst the infusions made using the roots are recommended for the treatment of several respiratory problems such as catarrh, bronchitis and sinusitis. It would also seem to provide effective relief for haemorrhoids.

Rumex lunaria.

PLOCAMA PENDULA

Family
RUBIACEAE (BEDSTRAW)

Plocama pendula Ait.
Spanish common name: BALO.

Plocama pendula.

Occurring throughout the archipelago, this Canary endemic is commonly found on all islands except Lanzarote and Fuerteventura. A shrub growing to a height of up to 4 metres, it has fragile, hanging branches and is characterised by the bad smell given off by the latter when split. Its filiform, rather fleshy, green leaves can be up to 5 cm long. The whitish flowers it bears are minute – both those growing in an axillary position and those appearing terminally at the ends of the youngest branches. *Plocama pendula* features a five to seven-lobed corolla and fruit in the shape of small globular berries, the latter being translucent at first and turning a blackish hue when ripe. This species grows above all on the ravine beds of the lower-lying areas of the islands. Its fruit constitutes the staple diet of a number of reptile species found on the archipelago during the dry season.

CAMPYLANTHUS SALSOLOIDES

Family
SCROPHULARIACEAE (FOXGLOVE)

Campylanthus salsoloides (L. fil.) Roth.
Spanish common name: ROMERO MARINO.

'he distribution of this member of the foxglove family is restricted to Cape 'erde and all the islands of the Canary archipelago, except for El Hierro, vhere it has not been reported. This is an evergreen shrub whose green ranches are flexible when young. It features linear, somewhat fleshy, right green leaves. Its flowers are grouped into terminal racemes, the ontrast between their violet-pink petals and their yellowish interior being true spectacle. *Campylanthus salsoloides* comes into bloom in late summer. 'ypically found in xeric, exposed environments of the lower-lying areas of ne islands, it is quite frequently used in the local parks and gardens. It is sted in Annexe II of the Flora Order.

Campylanthus salsoloides.

KICKXIA SCOPARIA

Family
SCROPHULARIACEAE (FOXGLOVE)

Kickxia scoparia (Brouss. ex Spreng.) Kunk. et Sund.

This Canary endemic occurs on the islands of La Palma, La Gomera, Tenerife and Gran Canaria. Herbaceous in appearance, this erect plant features sparse, slender green branches. It has linear, greyish-green leaves that are extremely prone to falling. Arranged singly on the stem, the flowers borne by *Kickxia scoparia* are highly characteristic – as are those of all the species of this genus – on account of their having one more or less straight, spur-shaped petal. Its fruit take the form of ovoid capsules.

Kickxia scoparia.

FORSSKAOLEA ANGUSTIFOLIA

Family
URTICACEAE (NETTLE)

Forsskaolea angustifolia Retz.
Spanish common name: HIERBA RATONERA.

orsskaolea angustifolia.

'his Canary endemic enjoys a wide distribution on the archipelago, ccurring as it does on all the islands. A subshrub-like species, it varies reatly in size, ranging from just a few centimetres to up to 2 metres when onditions are favourable. It features simple, alternate, dentate, spiny eaves that are dark green above and thickly hairy underneath. Its minute lowers are clustered into small, pinkish-hued axillary inflorescences. The ruit borne by this plant is also tiny. *Forsskaolea angustifolia* is a species haracteristic of arid areas and is very frequently found in disturbed nvironments, a fact which highlights its rather ruderal nature. Renowned mongst rural communities for its medicinal properties, this species is sed in the form of infusions which, made from any part of the plant, have sudoriferous (sweat-inducing), antipyretic and anti-inflammatory effect, nd are recommended above all for lung and bladder complaints.

ASPARAGUS PASTORIANUS

Family
LILIACEAE (LILY)

Asparagus pastorianus Webb et Berth.
Spanish common name: ESPINA BLANCA.

Asparagus pastorianus.

Widely distributed outside the Canary archipelago, this species is found on all the islands except La Palma and El Hierro. A procumbent, climbing shrub, it affords a rather tangled appearance and has densely arranged, thorny branches. A characteristic feature of this genus is the presence of cladodes, which are small, modified stems closely resembling ordinary leaves. In this case, the linear, non-spiny cladodes are up to 5 mm long and appear in dense fascicles in the axils of the thorns. *Asparagus pastorianus* has small white flowers clustered in axillary racemes and bears a reddish-hued, fleshy fruit. It is used medicinally on account of both the diuretic properties displayed by infusions prepared with its roots and its value as a weight-reducing agent (in which case the infusion made by boiling its stems in white wine is taken on an empty stomach). A protected species under regional legislation, it is listed in Annexe II of the Flora Order.

THERMOSCLEROPHYLLOUS COMMUNITIES

orming part of the ecological
nation of the vegetation of
e Canary Islands, a
ansitional zone is to be
stinguished that is
articularly interesting on
ccount of its floristic content
nd the diversity of its
ssociated plant communities.
nis zone is that marked by the
resence of what are
rmations of great biogeographical importance, namely the
ermosclerophyllous woods. These formations have experienced a drastic
duction in their potential surface area and have lost much of their former
uality, which is largely to be explained by the fact that their original
istribution areas have turned out to be those best suited for the growing of
rops and the establishment of human settlements.

hese thermosclerophyllous communities are seen to develop in what can be
rmed moderate environmental conditions, both with regard to temperature
average annual temperatures ranging from 16 to 18 °C) and hydric stress
5-month water deficit and average annual precipitation of under 500 mm).
hey occupy a strip of land lying at an altitude of between 50 and 500 m,
epending on the orientation of the terrain. Another characteristic feature of
is type of formation is that it does not constitute a homogenous community,
ut rather varies from one location to another with regard to the predominant
ements of its flora. Thus, the following communities can be distinguished:

Wild olive groves or "Acebuchales" *(Olea europaea* spp. *cerasiformis).*
hese formations exhibit a relatively significant distribution, above all on the
land of Gran Canaria, and are at present showing signs of recovery, owing to
e decline of traditional activities. The most interesting examples of the
cebuchales are situated in areas of medium altitude in the north-eastern
ections of the islands.

Mastic thickets or "Almacigares" *(Pistacia atlantica).* Displaying at present a
mited distribution, the finest examples of these formations are to be seen in
e western half of Gran Canaria.

Lentisc thickets or "Lenticales" *(Pistacia lentiscus).* This community is best
presented by the formations occurring in north-eastern Gran Canaria, at an
titude of between 300 and 500 metres.

Palm groves or "Palmerales". *(Phoenix canariensis).* Growing as they do in
vourable areas of the basal layer and in much of the territory occupied by
e so-called transitional vegetation, palm groves are found at altitudes under
00 m in coastal areas that are not directly influenced by the sea, on ravine
oors and channels and on hillsides affording sufficient soil moisture. The
anary Islands are graced by excellent manifestations of this formation, above
ll on Gran Canaria and La Gomera.

Juniper groves or "Sabinares" *(Juniperus turbinata* ssp. *canariensis).*
espite having once enjoyed a wide distribution in most of the archipelago
of which excellent examples still remain on La Gomera and El Hierro –, this
rmation cannot really be claimed to exist on Tenerife, La Palma and Gran
anaria, where junipers are seen to appear in relative isolation.

JUNIPERUS TURBINATA SSP. CANARIENSIS

Family

CUPRESSACEAE (CYPRESS)

Juniperus turbinata ssp. *canariensis*
(Guy.). Rivas-Mart. et al.
Spanish common name: SABINA (CANARY JUNIPER).

Juniperus turbinata.

This subspecies is endemic to Madeira and the Canary Islands, where it occurs on La Palma, La Gomera, El Hierro, Tenerife and Gran Canaria. A tree featuring a thick, twisting trunk, it has a rough, grey to reddish-brown bark that peels off in strips. Its scale-like, triangular, overlapping leaves have a hardened apex and form a dark green crown. Whereas the male flowers are arranged in small cones at the tips of the branches, the female ones grow in the axils of the latter. The tree bears globular fruits (called *arcéstidas)* which on ripening turn a reddish-grey colour. Highly valued on account of its solid, durable wood, this species has been employed in cabinet-making and the manufacture of furniture and roofing. Used by the pre-Hispanic inhabitants for the production of weapons, this wood has been found in their graves. The medicinal value of this tree resides in the abortion-inducing and sudoriferous properties of its cooked fruit and the use of its bark in infusions as a remedy for kidney diseases. Despite having once formed a number of rather large woods, the extension of this species on the islands has since been drastically reduced. The best surviving examples of sabinares or Canary juniper woods are found on the islands of El Hierro and La Gomera. Particularly noteworthy amongst these is the *dehesa* of El Hierro, sparse plantations comprising very old specimens that have taken on some very

Juniperus turbinata.

nciful forms due to the constant action of the wind. A truly
ectacular, singular tree, *Juniperus turbinata* was declared the official
tural plant symbol of the island of El Hierro by virtue of Regional Act
1991 dated 30th April and . This species enjoys protection under
gional legislation (Annexe II of the Flora Order).

BOSEA YERVAMORA

Family
AMARANTHACEAE (AMARANTH)

Bosea yervamora L.
Spanish common name: HIERBAMORA.

Bosea yervamora.

Found throughout the archipelago, this Canary endemic is a small shrub that often grows in a hanging fashion. Its dense, slender, greenish branches reach lengths of up to 3 m. Arranged alternately on the stems, i leaves are green, widely lanceolate and measure up to 10 cm long. *Bosea yervamora* is a dioecious species featuring small yellowish flowers arranged in racemes. Having a long flowering period, it produces fleshy, bright red fruits. A very abundant plant, it is characteristic of the thermophilous woodland environment, although it does also occur in other plant formations. This species has been widely used for medicinal purposes on account of its analgesic and anti-inflammatory properties.

PISTACIA ATLANTICA

Family
ANACARDIACEAE (SUMAC)

Pistacia atlantica Desf.
Spanish common name: ALMÁCIGO.

)ccurring on all the islands of the Canary archipelago except La Palma nd El Hierro, this tree is also found in Northern Morocco. Densely ranched, it can grow to heights of over 10 metres. The bark of its trunk ·atures a characteristic rough texture and greyish colour. Its compound, enerally deciduous leaves reach lengths of up to 15 cm and are dd-pinnate, that is, they have an uneven number of leaflets. The leaflets re a bright green colour, occasionally with a hint of red, and widely nceolate. Commonly found on the leaves of this tree are the bright red alls or swellings caused by insect parasites. *Pistacia atlantica* is a dioecious pecies having both male and female individuals. The male flowers are a ellowish colour, whereas the female ones feature a reddish hue. In either ase, they are grouped into elongated racemes. The bright red, spherical, omewhat fleshy fruits are clustered into tightly-packed racemes measuring ver 20 cm in diameter. Having a flowering period embracing the spring ionths, this species is an ssential component of ie thermophilous oodlands of the Canary slands, despite the fact iat its original istribution area has iminished considerably. i the past its wood was ighly regarded in abinetmaking and its esin was used medicinally n account of its analgesic roperties and the trengthening effect it has n gums. Furthermore, ie infusions prepared sing its branches and uits display nti-diarrhoeic and nticatarrhal properties. isted in Annexe II of ie Flora Order, this pecies is subject to rotection measures on a egional scale.

Pistacia atlantica.

PISTACIA LENTISCUS

Family
ANACARDIACEAE (SUMAC)

Pistacia lentiscus L.
Spanish common name: LENTISCO (MASTIC TREE, LENTISC).

Pistacia lentiscus.

Enjoying a wide distribution in the Mediterranean area, the mastic tree i to be found throughout the Canary archipelago, with the exception of La Palma and El Hierro. An evergreen species, it is smaller in stature than *Pistacia atlantica,* from which it can be distinguished by means of its abruptly-pinnate leaves and the winged rachises of the latter. Moreover, its inflorescences and fruit racemes are comparatively smaller. *Pistacia lentiscus* is a characteristic element of the thermophilous woodlands of the Canary Islands (above all on Gran Canaria), where it forms groves with wild olives. Its soft leaves and stems are renowned for their astringent properties, whilst its resin, heated up with white wine and water, was used in the past to combat tuberculosis. Species protected under regional legislation (Annexe II of the Flora Order).

BUPLEURUM HANDIENSE

Family
APIACEAE (PARSLEY)

Bupleurum handiense (Bolle) Kunk.

To be pinpointed as occurring on the islands of Fuerteventura and Lanzarote, this Canary endemic is a densely-branched, small-proportioned woody shrub. Its simple, greyish-green, widely ovate, leathery leaves are characterised by their distinct venation comprising up to seven parallel veins. It features yellow terminal inflorescences each containing from 4 to 6 flowers. The fruit it bears is elongated and black. A rare plant exclusive to rocky crags and escarpments, it is classified as a vulnerable species and as such enjoys protection under both Community and regional legislation (Annexe I of the Berne Agreement; Annexe II of the Habitats Directive; Annexe I of the Flora Order).

Bupleurum handiense.

CHEIROLOPHUS DURANII

Family
ASTERACEAE (DAISY)

Cheirolophus duranii (Burch.) Holub.
Spanish common name: CABEZÓN.

Exclusive to the island of El Hierro, very few populations of this species remain. A woody shrub that is branched from its base, it reaches a height of up to 1 metre. Whereas its older branches are covered in a brown bark, the younger shoots are a whitish hue. Its entire, subsessile, ovate-elliptic, dentate leaves are longer than they are wide. Borne on 10 cm-long peduncles at the end of the lateral branches, the inflorescences feature flower heads (capitula) arranged singly or in groups of 2 to 3. The cream-coloured, globular heads measure approximately 1.5 cm in diameter and boast highly characteristic scales, which in this case are ovate-oblong, over 7 mm long, complete with a yellowish, laciniate apical appendage. *Cheirolophus duranii* blooms in summer. A rare and endangered species of ornamental value, it is regarded as meriting the strictest protection measures (Annexe I of the Berne Agreement; listed in Annexe II of the Habitats Directive; classified as "in danger of extinction" in the National Catalogue of Endangered Species; Annexe I of the Flora Order).

Cheirolophus duranii.

GONOSPERMUM FRUTICOSUM

Family
ASTERACEAE (DAISY)

Gonospermum fruticosum (Buch) Less.
Spanish common name: FARO, CORONA DE REINA.

Gonospermum fruticosum.

The distribution of this spectacular plant is limited to the western islands of the Canary archipelago (La Palma, El Hierro, La Gomera and Tenerife). An abundantly branched shrub growing up to a metre high, its stem is covered with a firm greyish-hued bark. Its reddish younger shoots are somewhat sticky to the touch, whilst its bright green leaves are more or less lanceolate and bipinnatisect, with dentate secondary pinnae. The bright yellow flower heads of this plant are under 5 mm in diameter, have no ligules (unlike the daisy species) and are grouped into dense inflorescences measuring over 5 cm across. *Gonospermum fruticosum* blooms during the months of spring. It is commonly found on the rocky crags and slopes of the lower-lying northern areas of the islands. A plant of medicinal value, it is renowned for the curative properties (in cases of catarrh and stomach complaints) of infusions made with its flowers and leaves.

TANACETUM FERULACEUM

Family
ASTERACEAE (DAISY)

Tanacetum ferulaceum (Webb) Sch. Bip.
Spanish common name: MAGARZA PEGAJOSA (TANSY).

C

Tanacetum ferulaceum.

This Canary endemic exclusive to the island of Gran Canaria has two varieties, namely *Tanacetum ferulaceum,* characteristic of the southern region of the island; and *Tanacetum latipinnum,* which occurs in the west. The species of this genus can be differentiated from those of the *Argyranthemum* genus on account of their having fewer, smaller ligules in their flower heads. A densely branched, woody shrub, it grows to heights of over 50 cm. Its sticky green leaves, measuring up to 8 cm long, are divided, generally uni-or bipinnatisect, the individual segments or pinnae of the leaves being narrow and linear in shape. The flower heads, which usually feature eight white ligules and a bright yellow centre, are clustered into highly spectacular terminal inflorescences. *Tanacetum ferulaceum* bears fruit in the form of cylindrical cypselas displaying 5 visible veins. Species protected under regional legislation (Annexe II of the Flora Order).

MAYTENUS CANARIENSIS

Family
CELASTRACEAE (SPINDLE TREE)

Maytenus canariensis (Loes.) Kunk. et Sund.

Maytenus canariensis.

With the exception of Lanzarote, this Canary endemic can be seen on all the islands of the archipelago. A woody, evergreen shrub, it can reach a height of up to 4 metres. It has entire, simple, leathery, bright green leaves with serrate margins. The small pale yellow-green flowers borne by this plant feature an axillary cymose arrangement. Its fruit is globular, divided into three loculi, and has a pale green colour that turns light brown on ripening. *Maytenus canariensis* is characteristic of transitional areas and is found in the most xeric and thermophilous environments of the formations known as *monteverde*. The fruit of this plant has been used in the treatment of skin problems (crushed into a paste and applied directly onto the skin), whilst the infusion prepared using its leaves would appear to have anti-rheumatic properties. Species protected under regional legislation (Annexe II of the Flora Order).

CONVOLVULUS FLORIDUS

Family
CONVOLVULACEAE (BINDWEED)

Convolvulus floridus L. fil.
Spanish common name: GUAYDIL.

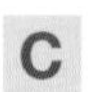

Convolvulus floridus.

This Canary endemic displays a certain degree of morphological variability, as a result of which up to four distinct varieties have been considered, all of which occur throughout the archipelago. A tall, densely branched shrub, it grows to a height of between 2 and 4 metres and features erect branches. Its greyish-green leaves are entire, alternate and linear to oblong in shape. *Convolvulus floridus* blooms profusely, having as it does dense terminal inflorescences comprising numerous bell-shaped flowers that measure over 1 cm in diameter and which are a white or slightly pinkish hue. Capsular fruits. Owing to the spectacular nature of its flowering, this species is very often grown as an ornamental plant and is a common sight in the parks and gardens of the Canary Islands.

CONVOLVULUS GLANDULOSUS

Family
CONVOLVULACEAE (BINDWEED)

Convolvulus glandulosus (Webb) Hallier.

Convolvulus glandulosus.

This species of the Bindweed family occurs only in the southern region of the island of Gran Canaria. It is a densely branched, leafy, climbing subshrub. It features entire, alternate, lanceolate, greyish-green, more or less glabrous leaves that are characterised by their numerous glands. The plant's inflorescences comprise no more than 1 or 2 small, bell-shaped, pale pink flowers. *Convolvulus glandulosus* blooms from April to June. A rare species protected under Canary Island legislation (Annexe II of the Flora Order).

CONVOLVULUS LOPEZSOCASI

Family
CONVOLVULACEAE (BINDWEED)

Convolvulus lopezsocasi Svent.
Spanish common name: CORREGÜELA DE FAMARA.

Convolvulus lopezsocasi.

As its common name would suggest, this Canary endemic is restricted to small enclaves in the north of the island of Lanzarote. Affording a rather tangled appearance, it is a lianoid species featuring glandular, elliptic-lanceolate, green leaves measuring up to 6 cm in length. Its inflorescences are composed of a varying number of flowers (maximum 6) and boast a pale violet bell-shaped corolla. This species is of great ornamental value and is therefore used in the parks and gardens of the island. An endangered species within its natural habitat, *Convolvulus lopezsocasi* enjoys protection under regional legislation (Annexe I of the Flora Order), the Berne Agreement (Annexe I) and the Habitats Directive (in which it is regarded as a Priority Species).

BRYONIA VERRUCOSA

Family
Cucurbitaceae (Gourd)

Bryonia verrucosa Dryand.

Bryonia verrucosa.

This climbing plant endemic to the Canaries occurs on all the islands except for those lying farthest to the west (Fuerteventura and Lanzarote). It has long, green, slender stems featuring spring-like tendrils for support. Palmate in shape and rough to the touch, its large, herbaceous, simple leaves are arranged alternately and have long stalks. The flowers borne by *Bryonia verrucosa* have 5 yellow petals with greyish edges and, measuring over 1 cm in diameter, are grouped loosely into axillary inflorescences. Its highly conspicuous fruit, reminiscent of small marrows, are less than 3 cm across. Green with yellowish stripes, they turn an orange-yellow colour when ripe. The flowering period of this plant spans the winter and spring months. Summer brings the appearance of the toxic fruit, whose rhizomes are used medicinally as an emetic and whose roots have anti-rheumatic properties.

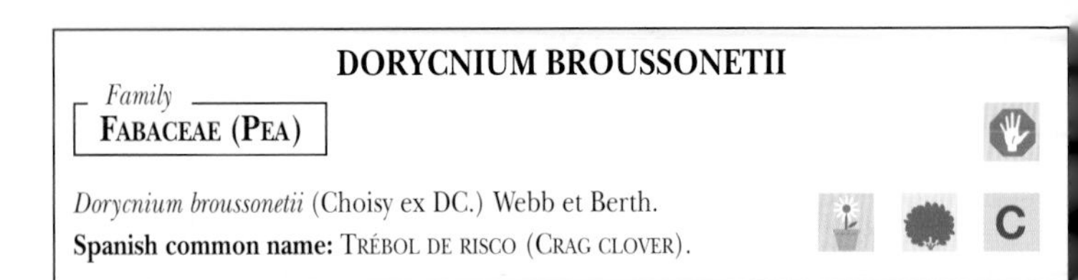

DORYCNIUM BROUSSONETII

Family
FABACEAE (PEA)

Dorycnium broussonetii (Choisy ex DC.) Webb et Berth.
Spanish common name: TRÉBOL DE RISCO (CRAG CLOVER).

Dorycnium broussonetii.

This Canary endemic belonging to the pea family occurs on the islands of Gran Canaria and Tenerife, although it is a very rare species on the former. A densely branched, woody perennial shrub, it can grow to a height of over a metre and a half. It has trifoliolate leaves whose more or less ovate lobes are up to 4 cm long. Appearing basally on the leaves are two cordate stipules. The whitish, pink-striped flowers borne by *Dorycnium broussonetii* are grouped into dense racemes featuring clusters of approximately eight flowers. The flowering period of this plant spans the winter and spring months. Its fruit takes the form of cylindrical, straight legumes or pods that are brown when ripe and reach lengths of up to 5 cm. Typically found in shady environments on the rocky crags and stony slopes of the lower-lying areas of the island, this species is of great ornamental value and has also been used as a fodder plant. It enjoys regional-scale protection on being listed in Annexe I of the Flora Order.

TELINE NERVOSA

Family
FABACEAE (PEA)

Teline nervosa (Esteve) A. Hans. Et Sund.
Spanish common name: RETAMA PELUDA (HAIRY BROOM).

This most singular broom is exclusive to the island of Gran Canaria, where but a few populations remain. Densely branched from its base, it is a shrub that can reach heights of over 2 metres. Its pale-green, trifoliolate leaves are covered in a smooth layer of hair or tomentum that is much more noticeable on the undersides of the blades. The plant's leaflets display a marked venation featuring somewhat revolute margins and its yellow flowers are grouped into dense terminal racemes. The fruit borne by *Teline nervosa* takes the shape of small, hairy, brownish-grey pods measuring up to 4 cm long. Flowering as it does from January to April, this is a rare species occurring in very few populations that is regarded as being in danger of extinction. Consequently, it is subject to strict protection measures (being listed in Annexe I of the Berne Agreement and Annexe II of the Flora Order; and classified as "in danger of extinction" in the National Catalogue of Endangered Species). Owing to its considerable ornamental value, *Teline nervosa* can be found in some of the parks and gardens of the islands.

Teline nervosa.

GLOBULARIA SALICINA

Family

GLOBULARIACEAE (GLOBULARIA)

Globularia salicina Lam.

Spanish common name: MOSQUERA, LENGUA DE PÁJARO.

Globularia salicina.

Occurring on La Palma, La Gomera, El Hierro, Tenerife and Gran Canaria, this Macaronesian endemic is widely distributed on all except the latter of these islands. A densely branched shrub standing over 1.5 m high, it features lanceolate, bright green leaves arranged alternately on the branches. Its bluish-hued flower heads, measuring less than 1.5 cm across, are shortly petiolate and are located in the leaf axils appearing on the terminal sections of the branches. *Globularia salicina* has a very long flowering period that lasts from spring to late autumn.

HYPERICUM CANARIENSE

Family
HYPERICACEAE (ST JOHN'S WORT)

Hypericum canariense L.
Spanish common name: GRANADILLO, SANJUANERO.

'his spectacularly flowering shrub is found on all the islands of the
ırchipelago except Lanzarote and Fuerteventura. Its displays a certain degree
ıf morphological variability, as a result of which three different varieties have
ıeen described. A densely branched plant measuring up to 3 metres high,
he bark covering its branches is a pale brown colour. Its simple, entire,
ppositely arranged, linear to lanceolate leaves are glandless on their margins
.nd grow up to 8 cm long. *Hypericum canariense* bears highly conspicuous
lowers which, measuring up to 2 cm in diameter, comprise 5 bright yellow
ıetals, above which numerous stamens stand out. These flowers are grouped
ogether in dense, tightly-packed inflorescences appearing on the terminal
ections of the branches. The fruits of this shrub are globular capsules that on
ipening take on a dark brown colour and divide into four valves so as to aid
he release of its small seeds. A characteristic feature of this species is the fact
hat it loses its foliage during the summer months, its leaves changing in
olour from green to a reddish hue. Environmental conditions permitting,
Iypericum canariense has a long flowering period. It has been used both in
arming as a livestock fodder plant and in medicine due to the anxiolytic
anxiety-reducing) properties of its leaves and flowers.

Hypericum canariense.

SIDERITIS INFERNALIS

Family
LAMIACEAE (MINT)

Sideritis infernalis Bolle.

C

Sideritis infernalis.

This Canary endemic is exclusive to Tenerife, its distribution being limited to small enclaves in the south-western region of the island. A woody stemmed subshrub, it measures up to 70 cm high. Its green, slender, membranous leaves are rough and woolly to the touch and ovate-lanceolate in shape. *Sideritis infernalis* has a sparse inflorescence in which small groups of its flowers are arranged in whorls. These flowers are tubular in shape and feature a white corolla culminating in reddish-brown coloured lips. Flowering from April to June, this is a very rare, scarce species that grows in precipitous, humid, shady environments. Regarded as a species in danger of extinction, it is protected under regional Canary Island legislation (Annexe I of the Order of the Flora).

SIDERITIS SPICATA

Family
LAMIACEAE (MINT)

Sideritis spicata (Pit.) Marrero.

'his Canary endemic occurs
nly on La Gomera, although it
s quite frequently observed on
his island at altitudes of
etween 100 and 1,000 metres.
n upright, somewhat compact,
ushion-forming subshrub, it
eatures stems covered in a
ense tomentum which endows
he plant with a cottony
ppearance. Its membranous,
etiolate, ovate and crenulate
regularly notched margin)
eaves have green upper sides
nd an underside that has the
ame cottony appearance as its
tems. *Sideritis spicata* has long
nflorescences, its flowers being
rouped into tightly-packed
vhorls and boasting a yellowish
ell-shaped corolla and small
ark-brown lips.

Sideritis spicata.

LAVATERA ACERIFOLIA

Family
MALVACEAE (MALLOW)

Lavatera acerifolia Cav.
Spanish common name: MALVA DE RISCO (CRAG MALLOW).

)f considerable ornamental value, this endemic shrub occurs throughout he archipelago with the exception of the island of El Hierro. It features wo varieties, namely *Lavatera acerifolia,* which is found on the vesternmost islands, and *Lavatera hariensis,* restricted to Lanzarote and 'uerteventura. A woody shrub branched right from its base, it reaches eights of over 2 metres. Its large, simple, long-stalked, light green leaves re palmate in shape, have irregularly serrate margins and are somewhat ough to the touch. Measuring up to 8 cm across, the flowers of this plant ave long peduncles and are arranged singly or in small axillary clusters. 'hey are characterised by 5 free-standing, pale mauve-coloured petals that

turn a darker shade towards their base and above which numerous fused stamens stand out in the shape of a elongated staminal column. Generally speaking, *Lavatera acerifolia* blooms in winter and spring, although its flowers can be seen almost all year round. Typically found in rather shady, precipitous areas, this ornamental species is protected under regional legislation (Annexe II of the Flora Order) and is a common sight in the parks and gardens of the Canary Islands.

Lavatera acerifolia.

JASMINUM ODORATISSIMUM

Family
OLEACEAE (OLIVE)

Jasminum odoratissimum L.
Spanish common name: JAZMÍN (JASMINE).

This Macaronesian endemic is found throughout the Canary archipelago except for the island of Lanzarote. Whilst being very common on the westernmost islands, it is very rare on Gran Canaria and Fuerteventura. A woody shrub, it features densely arranged, up-turned, rather flexible branches. It has alternate, compound, dark-green coloured leaves which, borne on a grooved stalk, comprise an odd number of leaflets (3 or 5) ranging in shape from oblong to obovate, the largest of which being the one situated at the end of the leaf. The yellow flowers of this jasmine have a tubular corolla culminating in 5 lobes and are arranged in small groups (1 to 4) in the leaf axils. The fruit of *Jasminum odoratissimum* is a fleshy, sticky, green-coloured berry that is turgid in the first stages of its growth and turns black on ripening. A highly ornamental species that blooms in winter and spring.

Jasminum odoratissimum.

OLEA EUROPAEA

Family
OLEACEAE (OLIVE)

Olea europaea ssp. *cerasiformis* (Webb et Berth.) Kunk. et Sund.
Spanish common name: ACEBUCHE (OLIVE).

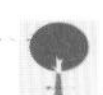

ɜearing a close relation to the Mediterranean olive, this tree occurs on ll the Canary Islands. A grey-barked species, it can reach a height of ver 6 metres. Growing opposite each other on either side of the ranches, its simple, entire, lance-shaped leaves are bright green above nd silvery-white beneath. The flowers of *Olèa europaea* feature a small alyx and a white, four-lobed, tubular corolla. They are arranged in small xillary clusters called panicles. Similar to an olive, its fleshy, ellipsoidal ruit ripens from green to black. This is a locally very common species haracteristic of the Canary thermophilous woodlands. It enjoys rotection under regional legislation (Annexe II of the Flora Order).

Olea europaea.

LIMONIUM SVENTENII

Family
PLUMBAGINACEAE (THRIFT)

Limonium sventenii Santos et Fernández.
Spanish common name: SIEMPREVIVA (SEMPERVIVUM).

Limonium sventenii.

This member of the thrift family (Plumbaginaceae) is endemic to north-western Gran Canaria. A small, branched bush growing to under a metre in height, it is characterised by its entire, rhomboidal, greyish-green leaves that are up to 15 cm long, rather fleshy, and feature short stalks. The leaves are arranged in rosettes, from which dense inflorescences arise on unwinged flowering stems. The flowers borne by *Limonium sventenii* display a bright-violet coloured tubular corolla. Having a flowering period stretching from December to June, this plant is regarded as a rare species on account of its being found in small, disperse populations. It is protected under both Community and regional legislation (considered a Priority Species by the Habitats Directive; listed in Annexe I of the Flora Order). It also appears in Annexe I of the Berne Agreement.

RHAMNUS CRENULATA

Family
RHAMNACEAE (BUCKTHORN)

Rhamnus crenulata Ait.
Spanish common name: ESPINO, ESPINERO.

Rhamnus crenulata.

'his Canary endemic of the buckthorn family occurs throughout the rchipelago. A woody shrub growing up to 2 metres high, its dense ranching lends it a rather tangled appearance. The bark of its branches s a reddish-grey colour. The simple, bright-green, short-stalked leaves of his plant are arranged into small groups on the branches and can be up o 5 cm long. They vary in shape, ranging from narrowly oblanceolate to bovate, have dentate margins and, unlike other species of the genus, re lacking in glands. *Rhamnus crenulata* features small, pale green lowers grouped sparsely into very abundant axillary inflorescences. Far nore conspicuous in nature are its fruits - small, fleshy drupes that take n a reddish hue when ripe. This species is characteristic of the ransitional areas of the islands, appearing above all on crags and slopes. 'ery abundant on the western islands, it has a more restricted listribution in the east of the archipelago. The roots of *Rhamnus renulata* are used medicinally in the form of an infusion to provide elief for stomach complaints.

MARCETELLA MOQUINIANA

Family
ROSACEAE (ROSE)

Marcetella moquiniana (Webb et Berth.) Svent.
Spanish common name: PALO DE SANGRE.

Marcetella moquiniana.

This singularly beautiful shrub is endemic to the Canary Islands, where its distribution is limited to the islands of La Gomera, Tenerife and Gran Canaria. A woody, branched plant, it stands up to 4 high. The most characteristic feature of this species is the appearance of glandular reddish hairs on the uppe branches, which endow the latter with their typical red colour (whence its popular name, lit.: "stick o blood"). Its pinnate, bluish-green coloured leaves are arranged in spectacular terminal rosettes and grow to a length of 20 cm. Each leaf comprises an odd number (7-15) of glaucous, petiolate leaflets with dentate margins. This is a dioecious species whose inflorescences take the form of a pendulous spike bearing a small number of minute flowers. Displaying a yellowish-green colour in the male plants, these flower clusters have a reddish hue in the female specimens. The small dry fruits borne on this shrub are winged and have a brownish-grey colour. Rarely seen growing wild, *Marcetella moquiniana* is characteristic of the ravines, slopes and cliffs of the lower-lying areas of the islands, and is a common feature of the parks and gardens of the Canaries. O considerable medicinal value, it is used above all as an astringent (a common remedy for digestive disorders is obtained by boiling the roots of this plant fo twenty minutes) and a cicatrisant or wound-healing substance (produced in the same way or by directly applying the liquid from the stems). This species is protected by the provisions of the regional Order regulating the conservation of wild plantlife and is listed in Annexe II of the latter.

WITHANIA ARISTATA

Family
SOLANACEAE (POTATO)

Withania aristata (Ait.) Pauq.
Spanish common name: OROBAL.

This medicinally very important species occurs on all the Canary Islands except Fuerteventura y Lanzarote, and is also found in Northern Africa. A highly variable shrub, it can take on tree-like proportions and reaches heights of up to 4 metres. It features densely arranged, fragile branches and a rough, greyish-coloured bark. Measuring up to 10 cm long, its large, lustrous, long-stalked, bright green leaves have an elongated heart shape. The small, bell-shaped, greenish-white flowers of this plant grow in the leaf axils, either singly or in small clusters, on more or less long peduncles. Its highly distinctive fruit, a fleshy green berry that turns an orange colour when ripe, is contained in a green receptacle, which is in fact the persistent calyx of the flower. Blooming throughout the winter and spring months, *Withania aristata* is renowned amongst the local population on account of its many medicinal properties. Thus, it has been used to relieve rheumatism, combat insomnia, encourage urination, and as a treatment for ear inflammation, eye problems and constipation. In most cases, infusions are prepared with the leaves and the bark, which are boiled and subsequently left to soak for at least a week. In order to stimulate urination, the fruit of this plant is normally eaten raw.

Withania aristata.

DRACAENA DRACO

Family
AGAVACEAE (AGAVE)

Dracaena draco (L.) L.
Spanish common name: DRAGO (DRAGON TREE).

Dracaena draco.

This famous tree owes its common name to the resemblance it bears to the monstrous mythical creature, a likeness observed by many authors in the scars lining its trunk and the crested culmination of its crown. Endemic to North Africa and the Macaronesian region, it occurs naturally on the islands of Gran Canaria, Tenerife and La Palma. *Dracaena draco* also appears on islands of the Cape Verde and Madeira archipelagos and has recently been reported in Northern Africa. A feature of juvenile specimens of the dragon tree is their unbranched appearance, branching not beginning until it has bloomed for the first time. Its simple, green, leathery leaves are arranged in terminal rosettes, whilst its numerous white flowers are densely clustered into highly conspicuous racemes. This species bears small, round, bright orange fruits and produces a distinctive reddish-coloured sap. The native peoples of the Canary Islands made defensive shields from the bark of this tree, which was also used in their burials. The medicinal properties of its sap were known way back in Roman times. Once dried and ground into a powder, the sap (or "dragon's blood") was used in the treatment of ulcers and haemorrhages and as a means of strengthening gums and cleaning teeth. It has also been employed in the production of lacquers, dyes and varnishes. Today, *Dracaena draco* is a very common sight in the parks and gardens of the archipelago, some specimens being particularly vorthy of note, such as those to be ound at Icod (Tenerife), Pino santo (Gran Canaria) and Buraca La Palma). Natural populations of this species, however, are omewhat depleted, as a result of which it has been classified as ulnerable. The dragon tree is protected under the provisions of egional legislation (Annexe II of he Flora Order), the Berne Agreement (Annexe I) and the Habitats Directive (Annexe IV). t was declared the official natural plant symbol of the island of Tenerife by virtue of Regional Act 7/1991, dated 30th April. A short ime ago, a new species of the dragon tree was discovered. Exclusive to Gran Canaria, it has been assigned the name of *Dracaena tamaranae.*

Dracaena draco.

PHOENIX CANARIENSIS

Family
ARECACEAE (PALM)

Phoenix canariensis Chab.

Spanish common name: PALMERA CANARIA (CANARY PALM).

Another of the official plant symbols of the Canary Islands, the Canary palm is distributed throughout the archipelago. This tree features a straight, thick trunk which, growing to a height of 15 to 20 metres, is typically covered in rhomboidal scars left by fallen leaves. The enormous leaves are clustered at the end of the trunk, thus giving rise to a dense, spherical crown. Measuring over 6 metres long, they are divided into a large number of widely linear, curled, stiff, green leaflets. Being a dioecious species, *Phoenix canariensis* has both male and female specimens. Whereas male individuals feature yellowish-white flowers grouped into dense, hanging inflorescences protected by a kind of sheath, the flowers borne on female trees take the form of orangish-red racemes. The fruit of the Canary palm, called *támaras,* resemble dates, but are somewhat smaller. Measuring up to 2 cm long, these orangish-yellow drupes, despite being edible, are not fleshy enough to be commercially viable. Flowering during spring and summer, this species is characteristic of the lower-lying areas of the Canaries, appearing above

Phoenix canariensis.

all at altitudes of under 600 me,tres. Having originally occurred in extensive formations, its distribution has since diminished. *Phoenix canariensis* has been of value to man ever since pre-Hispanic times, when its young tender leaves and its fruit were part of the diet of the indigenous peoples, who also used the leaves to make dresses, baskets, fishing nets, etc. Such a handicraft tradition has survived to the present day, the palm leaves acting as the raw material for the production of mats, hats, brooms, etc. Another ancient custom that still perdures, above all on the island of La Gomera, is that of extracting the sap (called *guarapo)* to make palm honey or eau de vie. Owing to its great beauty, the Canary palm is used as an ornamental species in parks and gardens throughout the world. The fruit of this tree displays certain medicinal properties, being used principally as a treatment for respiratory complaints (boiled támaras taken occasionally with goat's milk), stomach upsets or skin problems (in which case its juice is applied directly to the affected area). This species is protected under regional legislation (Annexe II of the Flora Order).

Communities of the subhumid montane layer: "Monteverde"

he term "monteverde" is used to refer both to the *laurisilva* woodland ormations and to the communities featuring myrtle and heather known here s *fayal-brezal,* which are equally to be found almost exclusively on the indward side of the islands, at an altitude of between 600 and 1,200 metres, here they are influenced by the 'sea of clouds' phenomenon caused by the rade Winds. Indeed, *monteverde* is characterised by what are truly optimal onditions for plant growth, the said formations never being subjected to ydric or thermal stress, recording as they do average annual temperatures f less than 15 °C and rainfall figures of around 1,000 mm. This supply of ater is further added to by horizontal precipitation, which can provide as uch as five times more water than rainfall itself. Whereas in the case of the *yal-brezal* formation the arboreal stratum is dominated by heather ("brezo", *rica arborea),* myrtle ("faya", *Myrica faya)* and the Canary holly ("acebiño", *ex canariensis),* the laurisilva communities display a greater diversity of oecies, amongst which the "til" *(Ocotea foetens),* the "viñátigo" *(Persea adica),* the "barbusano" *(Apollonias barbujana)* and the laurel ("laurel", *aurus azorica)* are particularly worthy of note.

lthough *monteverde* occurs on each of the five highest islands, the degree which it has been conserved varies from one to another. Thus, it can be een in all its glory on Tenerife (Anaga), La Gomera (Garajonay National ark) and La Palma (Los Tilos Reserve). On Gran Canaria, however, the riginal *monteverde* formations, as a result of their intense exploitation, have windled to such an extent that it has been estimated that the present-day elicts account for no more than 1% of their potential distribution.

ILEX CANARIENSIS

Family
AQUIFOLIACEAE (HOLLY)

Ilex canariensis Poir.
Spanish common name: ACEBIÑO (CANARY HOLLY).

Endemic to the Macaronesian region, the Canary holly occurs throughou the archipelago, with the exception of Lanzarote and Fuerteventura. A medium-sized evergreen tree standing up to 10 metres high, it is densely branched and features a rough, greyish brown bark. Its entire, alternate, 6 to 8 cm long, hard, lustrous leaves are ovate in shape and a bright green colour. The leaf margin is generally entire, although in young specimens it may bear spines. This is a dioecious species, even though the male and female flowers do not exhibit any morphological difference. White in colour, these flowers are small and grow in clusters at the ends of the branches. The fruit of *Ilex canariensis* is a red, rounded drupe measuring about 1 cm long and containing a small number of seeds. Of great foresta value, the tree blooms in spring and summer and is very frequently found in areas dominated by the *monteverde* formation, in particular those also featuring heathers and myrtles. It has traditionally been used to make farming tools and sticks and pitchforks for crops intended for export. The bark of this tree has cicatrisant (wound-healing) properties All use of the Canary holly is regulated by the provisions of regional legislation (Flora Order, Annexe III).

Ilex canariensis.

ARGYRANTHEMUM BROUSSONETII

Family
ASTERACEAE (DAISY)

Argyranthemum broussonetii (Pers.) Humphr.

Argyranthemum broussonetii.

Known for its spectacular daisy-like flower heads, this shrub occurs only on La Gomera, where it appears in the form of the subspecies *gomerensis,* and on Tenerife, where we find *Argyranthemum broussonetii.* A sturdy, densely branched plant, it reaches heights of over a metre. Its long, divided, elliptic, glabrous leaves measure up to 15 cm long and are usually bipinnatifid. The flowers borne by this shrub take the form of daisy-like capitula or flower heads which, being over 2 cm in diameter, are composed of white ligules and a bright yellow central disc and are arranged into more or less dense inflorescences. *Argyranthemum broussonetii* is a relatively abundant, highly ornamental species that is often planted in the parks and gardens of the Canary Islands. It is protected under regional legislation (Annexe II of the Flora Order).

PERICALLIS APPENDICULATA

Family
ASTERACEAE (DAISY)

Pericallis appendiculata (L. fil.) B. Nord.
Spanish common name: FLOR DE MAYO, ALAMILLO, PALOMERA.

Pericallis appendiculata.

This singular Canary endemic is found throughout the archipelago with the exception of Lanzarote and Fuerteventura. An evergreen plant, it is woody at its base and features herbaceous younger shoots. Its stems are covered in a dense layer of hair which confers them a whitish appearance. The long-stalked, oval-shaped, dentate leaves of *Pericallis appendiculata* are bright green above and have hairy, white undersides with very prominent veins. Its flower heads are typically small and boast white ligules and a yellow central disc. Varying in number from 5 to 30, these heads are arranged into terminal clusters. Flowering in the summer and autumn months, this species is characteristic of shady, moist environments and, avoiding exposed or sunny areas, occurs within the *monteverde* formations. An additional, highly endangered variety, *Pericallis preauxiana,* has been reported on Gran Canaria. This plant is listed in Annexe II of the regional Order regulating the conservation of wild plantlife.

PERICALLIS WEBBII

Family
Asteraceae (Daisy)

Pericallis webbii (Sch. Bip.) Bolle.
Spanish common name: Flor de mayo.

[E]ndemic to Gran Canaria, this [s]pecies occurs in abundance in [t]he northern part of the island. [I]t is an herbaceous perennial [t]hat varies greatly in size. Its [l]arge, entire, simple, longly [p]etiolate, green leaves measure [u]p to 15 cm across, are almost [c]ircular (orbicular) in shape [a]nd have sinuate margins. [A]rranged into clusters of 10 to [2]0, the daisy-like flowers of *[P]ericallis webbii* are relatively [s]mall, measuring 1 to 2 cm in [d]iameter, and exhibit [p]inkish-white to lilac-pink [l]igules and a dark purple [c]entral portion. This species has [a] certain ornamental value.

Pericallis webbii.

ECHIUM CALLITHYRSUM

Family
BORAGINACEAE (FORGET-ME-NOT)

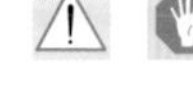

Echium callithyrsum Webb ex Bolle.
Spanish common name: TAJINASTE AZUL (BLUE VIPER'S BUGLOSS).

Found exclusively on the island of Gran Canaria, this viper's bugloss has a limited, very local distribution, its scattered populations occurring at altitudes of between 700 and 1,500 metres. A densely branched shrub, it stands up to 4 metres tall. *Echium callithyrsum* has bright green, lanceolate-ovate, entire (non-revolute) leaves whose size varies considerably (12-20 cm long) depending on the prevailing environmental conditions. These leaves are hairy, displaying large, thick bristles above and simple, short hairs underneath. They also feature prominent veins, above all on their underside. This species has an erect, cylindrical, basally slightly widened inflorescence, which is composed of a large number of bright blue flowers. Despite being a highly ornamental plant, it is not commonly used in gardens. The reduction of its habitat owing to the impact of human activities and the dispersed nature of its populations justify the classification of this viper's bugloss as a vulnerable species. Consequently, it is protected by regional legislation (Annexe II of the Flora Order).

Echium callithyrsum.

CANARINA CANARIENSIS

Family
CAMPANULACEAE (BELLFLOWER)

Canarina canariensis (L.) Vatke.
Spanish common name: BICÁCARO, BICACARERO.

Canarina canariensis.

This Canary endemic is found on all the islands of the archipelago except Fuerteventura and Lanzarote. It is a climbing plant whose annual fleshy stems dry up and die back at the end of spring and are subsequently replaced by new growth from its thick, tuberous root. The stems are hollow and contain a bitter, ill-smelling latex. Its simple, opposite, petiolate, rather pale green leaves are either triangular or lance-shaped and feature an irregularly serrate margin and prominent veins beneath. The highly characteristic flowers borne by *Canarina canariensis* are axillary, singly arranged and exhibit a large hammer-shaped style and an orange-red, bell-shaped corolla. Its edible fruits take the form of large, ovate, fleshy, reddish-orange berries. A highly ornamental plant well-known throughout the Canary Islands, it is often regarded as being one of the most representative elements of the Canary flora. This species is protected under regional legislation (Annexe II of the Flora Order).

SAMBUCUS PALMENSIS

Family
CAPRIFOLIACEAE (HONEYSUCKLE)

Sambucus palmensis Link.
Spanish common name: SAUGO, SAÚCO.

Sambucus palmensis.

This extremely rare small tree occurs in sparse populations on the island of La Palma, La Gomera, Tenerife and Gran Canaria. Boasting a dense foliage, as a rule it stands less than 5 metres high. It has knotty, arched branches that are somewhat rough to the touch and whose youngest shoots are a greenish-brown colour. Measuring up to 30 cm in length, its compound leaves always feature an odd number of leaflets (7 or less). The latter are glaucous-green in colour, oblong-lanceolate in shape, have a serrate margin and are covered with hair underneath. The inflorescences of *Sambucus palmensis* are dense, brightly-coloured umbels which, being 10 to 20 cm in diameter, comprise numerous flowers whose corollas are short white tubes measuring under 5 mm across. Its fleshy, black fruits are subglobular in shape and are less than 7 mm in diameter. This species is typically found in moist, shady areas of the better conserved *monteverde* communities and is used medicinally in the treatment of skin complaints. Today there are no more than twenty known wild specimens of this plant, which, together with its limited capacity for sexual reproduction (it produces only very few fertile seeds) implies that it is a highly vulnerable species that is to be regarded as being in danger of extinction. Consequently, it is subject to strict conservation measures, being listed in Annexe I of the Berne Agreement; considered a Priority Species in the Habitats Directive; and classified as "in danger of extinction" in the National Catalogue of Endangered Species. Sambucus palmensis also enjoys a high degree of protection under regional legislation (Annexe I of the Flora Order).

VIBURNUM TINUS SSP. RIGIDUM

Family
CAPRIFOLIACEAE (HONEYSUCKLE)

Viburnum tinus ssp. *rigidum* (Vent.) P. Silva.
Spanish common name: FOLLAO.

Endemic to the Canary Islands, this subspecies belonging to the honeysuckle family is found on La Palma, La Gomera, El Hierro, Tenerife and Gran Canaria. An evergreen shrub which, reaching a height of up to 5 metres, features a full, rounded crown composed of reddish-brown, up-turned branches. It has large, simple, opposite, dark green leaves that are ovoid to suborbicular in shape and have entire margins. Covered on both sides with a very fine layer of hair, the leaves are rough to the touch, leathery and have very prominent veins. The numerous white flowers, under 6 mm in diameter, are arranged into spectacular, tightly-packed, umbel inflorescences which themselves measure over 10 cm across. Equally striking are the oval-shaped fruits borne by *Viburnum tinus* ssp. *rigidum*, which, having a diameter of 6 to 7 mm, are a metallic violet colour and turn black when ripe. Blooming in spring, this shrub is renowned for its hard, flexible wood, which has been employed in craftwork and in the production of the sticks used in the time-honoured regional sport called *el juego del palo*. The infusions prepared using its leaves and fruits have antipyretical (fever-reducing) properties and also act as a laxative. The use of this plant is regulated by the Order governing the protection of the wild plantlife of the Canary Islands (Annexe III).

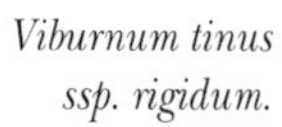

Viburnum tinus ssp. rigidum.

CONVOLVULUS CANARIENSIS

Family

CONVOLVULACEAE (BINDWEED)

Convolvulus canariensis L.

Spanish common name: CORREGÜELA DEL MONTE, CORREGÜELÓN.

Convolvulus canariensis.

Exclusive to the Canaries, this beautifully flowered bindweed occurs on all the islands except Fuerteventura and Lanzarote. A lianoid climbing plant featuring abundant foliage, it has woody, twisting basal branches that grow to lengths of over 10 metres. Its simple, alternate, petiolate, pale green leaves are more or less ovate in shape and reach lengths of up to 10 cm. Covered in a thick layer of hair both above and beneath, the leaves display a very prominent venation on their underside. When infested by mites, yellowish galls or swellings appear on the surface of the leaves. *Convolvulus canariensis* bears axillary inflorescences comprising a small number of flowers (no more than 7), which, bell-shaped, exhibit a densely hairy calyx and a white-centred, violet-edged corolla. This plant produces a pear-shaped fruit and blooms in the winter and spring months. An ornamental species, it is protected under regional legislation (Annexe II of the Flora Order).

ARBUTUS CANARIENSIS

Family
ERICACEAE (HEATH)

Arbutus canariensis Veill.
Spanish common name: MADROÑO (CANARY MADRONA).

elonging to the heath family, this tree – deemed by some to be the tree of the golden apples" known to the ancient Greeks – is a Canary ndemic that is found on all the islands except Fuerteventura and anzarote. A medium-sized evergreen, it can grow to a height of 5 metres. Perhaps the most outstanding feature of the tree is its trunk, hich is covered with a thin layer of bark that readily peels off in flakes reveal a reddish-brown, velvety stem that is very soft to the touch. Its arge, petiolate, lance-shaped leaves have serrate margins. Bright green nd lustrous above, they display a paler underside marked by a rominent midrib. Grouped into semi-erect panicles, the flowers borne y *Arbutus canariensis* feature fused petals and thus take the shape of mall, pinkish bells.

ts fruits are elatively large, leshy, edible, range-coloured erries, which ppear in dense lusters. The lowering period of his tree comes to an nd in summer, hich is when its ruit can be picked. rather ornamental pecies, its fruit is oted for its stringent roperties. It is rotected under egional legislation Annexe II of the lora Order).

Arbutus canariensis.

ERICA ARBOREA

Family
ERICACEAE (HEATH)

Erica arborea L.

Spanish common name: BREZO (HEATHER).

Erica arborea.

Reported to exist on all the islands of the archipelago, this species belonging to the heather family ha[s] a wide distribution encompassing the Canaries, Madeira, Africa and Europe. A tall evergreen tree reaching heights of up to 15 metres in very old specimens, it features densely-arranged, erect branches and a rough cracked bark when old. It has a large number of small, linear, dark green leaves that are arranged in whorls. *Erica arborea* owes its tiny, 4 mm-long, bell-shaped flowers to the union of its pinkish-white petals. These flowers are arranged into tightly-packed lateral racemes, thus ensuring a spectacular bloom, one in which the plant undergoes a dramatic colour change. The fruit takes the form of small, smooth, dark-coloured capsules. This species has played a very important role in the rural economy of the islands, being employed both as fodder and bedding for livestock, in the production of charcoal, and as a source of sticks and forks. Used medicinally on account of its anti-inflammatory properties, it is particularly recommended for the urinary tract and also has a soothing action to relieve the effects of insect bites. The use of this plant is regulated by regional legislation (Annexe III of the Flora Order).

EUPHORBIA LAMBII

Family
EUPHORBIACEAE (SPURGE)

Euphorbia lambii Svent.

his Canary endemic, a member of the spurge family, is exclusive to La omera, being sparsely distributed in the northern section of the island altitudes ranging from 500 to 1,000 metres. An evergreen shrub owing to a height of up to 2 metres, it has erect, slender, light brown anches. Its long, green, narrowly lanceolate leaves are arranged like settes at the ends of the branches. *Euphorbia lambii* displays yellowish, ore or less dense, terminal, umbel inflorescences. Its small, greenish owers feature considerably large, almost completely joined bracts. The uits borne by this spurge are pale brown capsules. All the parts of the lant contain a bitter, caustic latex. Its flowering period lasts from winter ntil late spring. A local, scarce species, the total number of specimens to e found is rather small, as a result of which it is included in Annexe I of e Berne Agreement and Annexe II of the EC Habitats Directive. It is bject to strict protection regulations under regional legislation Annexe I of the Flora Order).

Euphorbia lambii.

EUPHORBIA MELLIFERA

Family
EUPHORBIACEAE (SPURGE)

Euphorbia mellifera Ait.
Spanish common name: TABAIBA DE MONTE, ADELFA, ADELFA DE MONTE.

Euphorbia mellifera.

Constituting the only tree species of its genus to be found on the Canary Islands – on La Palma, La Gomera and Tenerife –, this member of the spurge family also occurs on the island of Madeira. Growing to a height c up to 15 metres, it features an erect, woody trunk that is terminally densely branched and has a rough, greyish-hued bark. As is the case with *Euphorbia lambii,* the leaves of this plant are arranged in dense clusters at the ends of its branches. Up to 30 cm long, these dark green, lanceolate leaves are slightly hairy on the underside. The small flowers of *Euphorbia mellifera* are grouped into terminal panicles and feature purple-colour bracts. Its fruit takes the form of large, rough, three-sectioned capsules. All parts of the plant contain a white, sticky latex that is used in the treatment of skin complaints. This species is typically found in very shady, humid areas of the best preserved environments of the *laurisilva* laurel forests. Only a very small number of specimens remain, as a result of which it is classified as being "in danger of extinction" in the National Catalogue of Endangered Species. It also enjoys protection under regional legislation (Annexe II of the Flora Order).

GERANIUM CANARIENSE

Family
GERANIACEAE (GERANIUM)

Geranium canariense Reut.
Spanish common name: PATA DE GALLO (CANARY GERANIUM).

Geranium canariense.

s is the case with most of the species of the *monteverde* formation, this anary endemic occurs on all the islands of the archipelago except for uerteventura and Lanzarote. Herbaceous in appearance, it is a perennial lant with a short woody trunk at its base. Its bright green, longly etiolate, very divided and irregularly palmately divided leaves can reach cm in diameter and are arranged in a large rosette. *Geranium canariense* isplays spectacular, branched, umbel-shaped inflorescences whose petalled (pentamerous) lilac-pink flowers measure up to 3 cm across. he stamens are fused at their base and feature pinkish filaments with red nthers. The ovary terminates in a pointed projection that is much longer han the flower itself and which on ripening divides into spiralling egments. Typically found in open areas within *monteverde* formations, this pecies is protected on a regional scale (Annexe II of the Flora Order).

SIDERITIS CANARIENSIS

Family
LAMIACEAE (MINT)

Sideritis canariensis L.

Sideritis canariensis.

Exclusive to the islands of La Palma, El Hierro and Tenerife, this species has two varieties, namely *Sideritis canariensis,* which occurs on all three islands; and *Sideritis pannosa,* which is only to be found on Tenerife. It is a woody, upright, more or less densely branched shrub. Its slightly yellowish green leaves are heart-shaped at the base and ovate at the top of the branches and feature a somewhat dentate margin. The underside of the leaves has a thicker covering of yellowish, branched hairs. The long inflorescences of this plant are either simple or basally branched and comprise sparsely arranged whorls of distant flowers. Each of these floral whorls, surrounded by a pair of linear bracts, contains many tubular flowers with yellowish corollas and dark-coloured lips. Of certain medicinal value, this species is protected under regional legislation (Annexe II of the Flora Order).

SIDERITIS MACROSTACHYA

Family
LAMIACEAE (MINT)

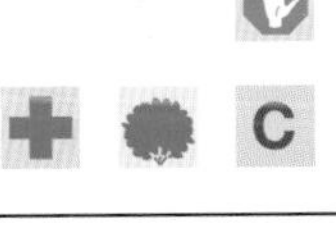

leritis macrostachya Poir.
anish common name: CHAHORRA DE MONTE, CHAHORRA DE ANAGA.

s shrubby species is exclusive to Tenerife, where its distribution is limited
he Anaga massif situated in the north-eastern part of the island. Standing
to 1 metre tall, it is an abundantly branched perennial featuring cottony
ng shoots. The large, simple, entire, long-stalked, cordate leaves measure
to 15 cm long and have regularly serrate margins. Greyish-green and
gh above, the leaves have an underside that is covered in a white layer of
: and has markedly prominent veins. The short, erect, branched
orescences of *Sideritis macrostachya* display a very compact, conical
ingement from which lanceolate bracts are seen to stand out. Its tubular
vers have a very hairy white calyx and a whitish-hued, brown-lipped
olla. The flowering period of this plant begins in January. Like all the
cies belonging to this genus, it is used medicinally, above all on account
he anticatarrhal properties of the infusions made from its leaves and
vers. Enjoys regional-scale protection (Annexe II of the Flora Order).

Sideritis macrostachya.

APOLLONIAS BARBUJANA

Family
LAURACEAE (LAUREL)

Apollonias barbujana (Cav.) Bornm.
Spanish common name: BARBUZANO.

Apollonias barbujana.

Popularly known as the "Canary ebony", this Macaronesian endemic belonging to the laurel family occurs on all the islands of the archipelag with the exception of Lanzarote. A fairly sizeable, densely branched perennial tree, it has large, lustrous, leathery, widely lanceolate, bright green leaves. Its young shoots are characterised by their transparent, reddish colour. Another distinguishing feature of this species – which as rule does not have glands associated with its veins – is the appearance o its leaves of galls or swellings when infested by mites. The small, whitish flowers are grouped into equally small terminal inflorescences. *Apollonia barbujana* blooms over such an extensive period that specimens in flowe can be found practically all year round. Its fruit takes the form of small drupes that turn black on ripening. A less demanding species, it displays greater ability to withstand adverse xeric conditions than other laurels s as *Persea indica* or *Ocotea foetens*. Highly regarded on account of its hardn and durability, its wood has been used in cabinet-making and in the manufacture of coffered ceilings, doors, etc. Enjoys protection on a regional scale (Annexe II of the Flora Order).

OCOTEA FOETENS

Family
LAURACEAE (LAUREL)

Ocotea foetens (Ait.) Baill.
Spanish common name: TILO, TIL.

haracteristic of the *laurisilva* laurel forests, this tree has a distribution at is restricted to the western Canary Islands, including Gran Canaria. aring to heights of up to 40 metres, it is densely branched and features umerous suckers at its base. Its bright green, widely lanceolate leaves nge in length from 8 to 12 cm and are characterised by the prominent ands appearing at the base of the midrib. The racemose inflorescences this species are composed of small, yellowish-white flowers, whilst its uit is reminiscent of an undersized acorn. *Ocotea foetens* blooms in ring and summer and is typically found in the shadiest and most umid areas of the laurel forests, where it occurs above all in ravine annels. It is a tree that has a great ability to condense moisture, a fact flected by rtain historical isodes such as e legend of "El aroé" on the land of El Hierro. his species is rotected on a gional scale, eing included in nnexe II of the lora Order.

Ocotea foetens.

PERSEA INDICA

Family
LAURACEAE (LAUREL)

Persea indica (L.) K. Spreng.
Spanish common name: VIÑÁTIGO.

Popularly known as the "Canary mahogany", this Macaronesian endemic occurs on all the islands of the archipelago with the exception of Lanzarote and Fuerteventura. It is a densely branched evergreen tree that stands up to 30 metres high. It features a dark grey trunk and large leaves that can reach lengths of over 20 cm. These entire, petiolate, lanceolate, lustrous leaves change from pale green to a reddish hue on ageing. The greenish-white flowers are relatively small and are arranged into loosely clustered terminal inflorescences, whilst the fruits are small drupes that turn black when ripe. Flowering in spring and summer, *Persea indica* is typically found in the most humid areas of the monteverde formations, even though it can survive in more xeric conditions. A tree of great forestal value, its wood was once used in boatbuilding and in cabinet-making. It is also known to have medicinal properties that are beneficial in the treatment of skin infections. On a regional level, this species is protected under the provisions of the Flora Order (Annexe III). It was declared the official natural plant symbol of the island of La Gomera by virtue of Regional Act 7/1991 dated 30th April.

Persea indica.

MYRICA FAYA

Family
MYRICACEAE (BAYBERRY)

Myrica faya Ait.
Spanish common name: FAYA, HAYA (MYRTLE).

Myrica faya.

'his Macaronesian pecies has been eported to occur on ll the islands of the :anary archipelago nd is also found in outhern Portugal. densely branched vergreen, it is a enerally small tree tanding from 3 to metres high. Its ark green leaves are eathery, slightly urved, narrowly anceolate and eature a netted enation. Growing midst the leaves which are arranged lternately on the tems – are the nflorescences of *lyrica faya,* omposed of umerous minute lowers. This is a lioecious species, hat is to say, one vhich has distinct male and female individuals. Its reddish, fleshy fruits re rough in appearance and can be eaten raw. Once dried and ground, hey are also used to make a kind of flour called *gofio.* Blooming in winter nd spring, this myrtle is one of the characteristic elements of the myrtle-eather formations known as *fayal-brezal* and readily colonises deforested ands. Mainly used as a source of sticks and forks for farming purposes, his tree is also of considerable medicinal value on account of both its otential as a remedy for catarrh and the astringent properties of its ruit. The use of the species is regulated throughout the archipelago nder regional legislation (Annexe III of the Flora Order).

PLEIOMERIS CANARIENSIS

Family
MYRSINACEAE

Pleiomeris canariensis (Willd.) A. DC.
Spanish common name: DELFINO.

Pleiomeris canariensis.

This most singular Canary tree has been reported to occur on the islands of La Palma, La Gomera, Tenerife and Gran Canaria, even though its existence has only been confirmed on the latter two. A small perennial standing from 2 to 4 metres tall (although it can reach a height of 15 metres), it features a large number of new shoots at its base. Its greyish trunk supports a dense arrangement of straight green branches. Measuring up to 25 cm long, its large, entire, simple, shortly stalked leaves are elliptic to oblong in shape and have prominent veins, above all on the underside. Somewhat leathery to the touch, they are a bright green colour. The cauline flowers and fruits of this tree are so called because they grow directly on its branches. The minute flowers, arranged into small inflorescences, are conferred a tubular appearance by their basally joined greenish petals. Less than 1 cm in diameter, the abundant, fleshy, globular fruits feature a flattened apex and are red when ripe. *Pleiomeris canariensis* blooms from December to March. Found in cleared, sunny areas, it is one of the species belonging to the marginal communities of the laurel forests. Its present-day state of conservation is somewhat worrying, due to the low density of individuals observed in its populations. This tree is protected under regional legislation (Annexe II of the Flora Order).

RHAMNUS GLANDULOSA

Family
RHAMNACEAE (BUCKTHORN)

Rhamnus glandulosa Ait.
Spanish common name: SANGUINO.

ndemic to the Macaronesian region, this member of the buckthorn ımily occurs on Madeira and on the islands of La Palma, La Gomera, 'enerife and Gran Canaria. A medium-sized evergreen tree standing 5 to 0 metres tall, it features a straight, densely branched, reddish-barked runk. Its simple, alternate, more or less ovate, dark green leaves are up to cm long and exhibit a reddish-hued grooved petiole and finely serrate nargins. A characteristic feature of this species is the small, prominent lands in the axils of the leaf veins, appearing mainly at the base of the leaf lade, although they may occur in more distal parts. The short, rather ense, subterminal inflorescences are composed of small, whitish flowers neasuring over 5 mm in diameter. The abundant fruit produced by this ree takes the form of short-stalked, bright red drupes. *Rhamnus glandulosa* looms in the winter and spring months. It is a rather scarce element ound in humid, sunny environments of the *monteverde* formations. Its fruit s known for its astringent properties. This species is protected within the Canary Islands (Annexe II of the Flora Order).

Rhamnus glandulosa.

BENCOMIA SPHAEROCARPA

Family
ROSACEAE (ROSE)

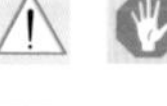

Bencomia sphaerocarpa Svent.

Bencomia sphaerocarpa.

This singularly beautiful shrub belonging to the rose family is exclusive to El Hierro, where it is found in the precipitous, humid areas of the northern section of the island. An erect, evergreen shrub standing 2 to 4 metres high, it is more or less densely branched. Its large leaves are termed odd-pinnate on account of their uneven number of leaflets (always over 13). The short-stalked green leaflets are lanceolate in shape, have serrate margins and are thickly silky. Being a dioecious plant, it features both male and female individuals. Its hanging inflorescences, in the shape of tightly-packed racemes, give rise to globular fruits, which, measuring over 5 mm across, are larger than those of other species of the genus. *Bencomia sphaerocarpa* blooms and produces its fruit during the winter and spring months. Only a very small number of individuals of this species remain as a result of which it is regarded as "endangered" in accordance with the categories established by the IUCN. Subject to strict protection measures, it is listed in Annexe I of the Berne Agreement and Annexe II of the EC Habitats Directive and is classified as being "in danger of extinction" in the National Catalogue of Endangered Species. It has been declared by regional legislation to be a species worthy of strict protection (Annexe I of the Flora Order).

PRUNUS LUSITANICA SSP. HIXA

Family
ROSACEAE (ROSE)

Prunus lusitanica ssp. *hixa* (Willd.) Franco.
Spanish common name: HIJA.

his member of the rose
.mily occurs on all the
anary Islands, with the
xception of Lanzarote
nd Fuerteventura, and is
lso found on Madeira. An
vergreen tree that usually
ands 10 metres tall
although it can reach
eights of up to 20 m), its
unk features a smooth
hitish bark with small,
longated, horizontal
nticels (breathing pores).
Old specimens very often
isplay aerial layering. The
ntire, simple, lanceolate
aves are large
measuring up to 15 cm
ong –, are borne on
eddish petioles and have
n irregularly serrate
nargin. Leathery to the
ouch, they are a shiny

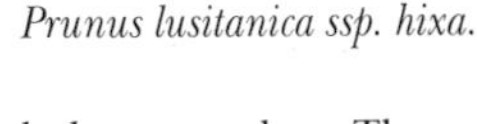
Prunus lusitanica ssp. hixa.

dark green colour. The small white flowers of *Prunus lusitanica* are grouped into elongated axillary pedunculate racemes reaching lengths of over 15 cm. Its fruit takes the form of ovoid to globular berries, which change from reddish to black on ripening. Particularly noteworthy on account of its spectacular bloom, this species is a characteristic element of the Canary laurel forests, although it is very rarely found on the islands of Gran Canaria and La Gomera. It enjoys protection under regional legislation (Annexe II of the Flora Order).

ISOPLEXIS CANARIENSIS

Family

SCROPHULARIACEAE (FOXGLOVE)

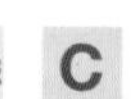

Isoplexis canariensis (L.) Loud.

Spanish common name: CRESTA DE GALLO.

Isoplexis canariensis.

The most abundant species of its genus, *Isoplexis canariensis* is a common sight on the islands of La Palma, La Gomera and Tenerife. A woody, evergreen, densely branched shrub, it stands up to a metre and a half tall. Its alternate, lanceolate to ovate, slightly leathery leaves have finely toothed margins. Bright green above, the leaves are a more subdued colour on their somewhat downy undersides. The highly conspicuous flowers of this plant are arranged in erect, very dense terminal inflorescences measuring over 30 cm long. Each flower is divided into two lips: a longer upper lip and a smaller, three-lobed lower lip. The tubular-shaped, 3 cm long corolla is a very bright orangish-red colour and contains four stamens featuring reddish filaments and yellow-coloured anthers. *Isoplexis canariensis* flowers from winter to early summer. It is a heliophilous (sun-loving) species that grows in open, sunny areas of the *monteverde* formations. As well as being of undoubte ornamental value, this plant is used for a wide range of medicinal purposes. I contains cardiotonic substances that have the effect of "toning up" the heart muscles, although they can be dangerous when administered in large doses. *Isoplexis canariensis* has also been used in the treatment of diabetes and varicose veins and would seem to have laxative properties. This is a protected species that is listed in Annexe II of the regional Order regulating the conservation of wild plantlife on the Canary Islands.

ISOPLEXIS CHALCANTHA

Family
SCROPHULARIACEAE (FOXGLOVE)

Isoplexis chalcantha Svent. et O'Shanahan.
Spanish common name: CRESTA DE GALLO.

Isoplexis chalcantha.

Found only in the relict *monteverde* communities of northern Gran Canaria, this shrub belonging to the foxglove family reaches a height of between 80 cm and 1 metre and features open, up-turned branches with subpersistent foliage. Its narrowly lanceolate leaves are green above, thickly hairy beneath, and display irregularly serrate margins. Either a reddish or coppery colour, the longly pedicellate flowers borne by this species, unlike those of *Isoplexis canariensis,* are grouped into a sparsely populated spike. At present only very few populations of this plant remain, occurring in association with *monteverde* relicts in somewhat exposed, sunny areas. According to the categories laid down by the IUCN, *Isoplexis chalcantha* is regarded as being "endangered". It is listed in Annexe I of the Berne Agreement and constitutes one of the Priority Species defined by the EC Habitats Directive. Furthermore, it has been classified as being "in danger of extinction" in the National Catalogue of Endangered Species. On a regional scale, this plant is deemed to merit strict protection measures (Annexe I of the Flora Order).

SOLANUM VESPERTILIO

Family

SOLANACEAE (POTATO)

Solanum vespertilio Ait.

Spanish common name: REJALGADERA.

This spectacularly flowered shrub is only found on the islands of Tenerife and Gran Canaria, being very rare on the latter. It is an erect, sparsely branched, evergreen plant that grows up to 1.5 metres tall and has thorny stems and leaf stalks. Its large, simple, alternate, ovate to rhomboidal leaves measure 5 to 15 cm long, are dark green and smooth above and yellowish-green and tomentose underneath. The flowers, appearing in clusters of 5 to 10, are arranged into usually terminal racemes. The four-lobed, more or less bell-shaped (campanulate) corollas are a vivid, bluish-violet colour with darker central edges. Standing out above each corolla are 5 bright yellow anthers, one of which, much longer than the others, is horn-shaped. *Solanum vespertilio* features pedicellate fruits, reminiscent of small tomatoes, that are grouped into hanging bunches. They are fleshy berries that change from green to a yellowish colour on ripening. This species is typically found on sunny, open slopes on the edges of the *monteverde* formations. Owing to its very sparse populations, it is regarded as being "vulnerable" and enjoys protection under regional legislation (Annexe II of the Flora Order).

Solanum vespertilio.

VISNEA MOCANERA

Family
THEACEAE (TEA)

Visnea mocanera L. fil.
Spanish common name: MOCÁN.

Visnea mocanera.

earing edible fruits, this species occurs on Madeira and all the islands of ie Canary archipelago except Lanzarote. It is a densely branched, vergreen tree ranging in height from 8 to 15 metres. Its simple, lternate, lanceolate-elliptic, dark-green leaves, measuring 5 to 8 cm long, ave serrate margins and are somewhat lustrous. *Visnea mocanera* bears nall, white, bell-shaped flowers that are grouped into small, somewhat anging, axillary racemes. Its edible, capsular, fleshy, oval-shaped fruit are greyish-red colour. The use of this plant by man dates back to pre-Iispanic times, when the native peoples made a paste called *charquequén* om its fruit *(yoyas)*. As well as being of ornamental value – as a result of hich it is sporadically planted in some of the gardens of the islands –, *'isnea mocanera* has numerous medicinal properties. It is protected on a egional level, being listed in Annexe II of the Flora Order.

GESNOUINIA ARBOREA

Family
URTICACEAE (NETTLE)

Gesnouinia arborea (L. fil.) Gaud.
Spanish common name: ESTRELLADERA, ORTIGÓN DEL MONTE.

Gesnouinia arborea.

This Canary endemic occurs on all the islands of the archipelago except Fuerteventura and Lanzarote. An evergreen, shrubby (occasionally tree-size) plant, it can reach a height of over 5 metres and is usually branched from its base. Its slender, easily-broken branches lend it a somewhat fragile appearance. Measuring up to 6 cm long, the alternately arranged, simple, entire, petiolate leaves are ovate to lanceolate in shape and feature three veins and a finely serrate margin. Displaying a rather dull green colour above, the leaves are somewhat downy on their undersides. *Gesnouinia arborea* has racemose inflorescences up to 25 cm long, each involucre (whorl of bracts) of which holds one female and two male flowers. The flowers are small and pinkish-hued. This hygrophilous (moisture-loving) plant is often found in ravine channels and on the very humid slopes of the *monteverde* formations. Although its flowering period usually spans the months of winter and spring, specimens in bloom can be found all year round. Of certain ornamental value, this species is protected under regional legislation (Annexe II of the Flora Order).

Communities of the dry montane layer: Pinewoods

inewoods are oligospecific wooded formations which on the Canary Islands re dominated by the Canary pine *(Pinus canariensis)*. This formation is to be ɔund on the islands of La Palma, El Hierro, Tenerife and Gran Canaria and xhibits an altitudinal distribution governed by the factor of orientation. Thus, n leeward-facing slopes, it stretches upwards from the thermophilous ɔrmations to an altitude of 2,000 metres or more. On the windward slopes, owever, it extends from above the *monteverde* level to the said height.
)ne of the characteristics of the pinewoods on the Canary Islands is the elatively low number of species to be found in the underbrush, although the xact floristic composition of the latter varies according to altitude and the ifferent environmental conditions prevailing on each island. Thus, the dominant nderwood species appearing on lower-lying terrain are the xerophytes haracteristic of transitional scrub, together with cistuses or "jaras" *(Cistus ionspeliensis)*. On the arid mountain-sides exposed to the full force of the sun, t heights of over 800 metres, the scrub growing amidst the pinewoods is ominated by cistuses *(Cistus monspeliensis* and *Cistus symphytifolius)* and burnums *(Adenocarpus* sp.), whereas in the more humid areas the heathers *Erica arborea)* and the "tagasastes" *(Chamaecytisus proliferus)* make their ppearance. Standing at an altitude of between 1,500 and 2,000 metres and xtremely limited in terms of floristic variety are what can be termed the enuine pinewoods, in which the only underbrush species to be found are the istuses *(Cistus symphytifolius)*, laburnums *(Adenocarpus* sp.), the "poleos" *Bystropogon origanifolius)* and the "corazoncillos" *(Lotus* sp.). Lastly, at the ighest altitudes there is a predominance of the mountain-top laburnums or rooms *(Spartocytisus supranubius)*, the pinewood itself becoming less dense wing to the more adverse environmental conditions inhibiting its growth.
he process of degradation affecting the pinewoods has led to the appearance of rge expanses of substitution scrubland featuring a predominance of spurge "tabaiba amarga", *Euphorbia obtusifolia)*, cistuses ("jaras", *Cistus monspeliensis)*, cidophilous scrub species such as thyme ("tomillo", *Micromeria* sp.) and the vender communities *(Lavandula* sp.). Meanwhile, in the more humid areas, ıanifestations of the "escobón" or *Chamaecytisus proliferus* are to be observed.

PINUS CANARIENSIS

Family
PINACEAE (PINE)

Pinus canariensis Chr. Sm. ex DC. In Buch.
Spanish common name: PINO CANARIO (CANARY PINE).

The distribution of the Canary pine is restricted to the Canary archipelago, where it occurs naturally on all the islands except for Fuerteventura and Lanzarote. A perennial tree species, it features medium-sized trunks ranging in height from 20 to 30 metres and measuring up to 1 metre in diameter, although in certain conditions they can grow to heights of 50 metres and have diameters of over 2 metres. Its reddish-hued bark is thick and cracked in appearance. Young individuals of the Canary pine exhibit a typically conical crown, which takes on a more umbrella-shaped aspect as the tree ages. The very slender, acicular (needle-shaped), pointed leaves grow up to 30 cm long and are grouped into bunches of three that appear above all on the new shoots. Male and female flowers are quite distinct, the former being arranged into short, yellowish-red, spike-shaped racemes, whereas the latter form cones measuring 10-20 cm. The fruit borne by *Pinus canariensis,* the pine cone, contains a large number of seeds (pine nuts) in each of its thick scales. Flowering in spring, this species is characteristic of the Canary pinewoods, occupying large expanses at altitudes of above 1,000 metres, although it also plays an important role in the colonisation of volcanic substrata, as is to be witnessed on the islands of La Palma and El Hierro. Owing to is magnificent properties, above all the quality and durability of its wood, the Canary pine has been a natural resource ever since pre-Hispanic times. Its softer wood was once employed in the manufacture of coal, whereas its heartwood (a very special wood formed by the accumulation of resins at the heart of the oldest pines) was used in cabinet making, carpentry, and in the production of coffered ceilings and roofing materials. Moreover, the Canary pinewoods in the past witnessed the burning of the heartwood of *Pinus canariensis* in order to extract its resin and thus obtain the tar or pitch that was used both for medicinal purposes and as a means of repairing boats and other vessels. For their part, the pine leaves furnished bedding for livestock and also served as a

Pinus canariensis.

Pinus canariensis.

:ertiliser and as a packaging material for the export of bananas. A tree of :onsiderable medicinal value, its buds are used in the preparation of nfusions or inhalants recommended for respiratory complaints such as)ronchitis or asthma, whilst its resin is employed in the removal of cysts. 3oth the use of the Canary pine and the protection measures it is subject :o are regulated by regional legislation (Annexe III of the Flora Order). :t was declared the official natural plant symbol of the island of La Palma)y virtue of Regional Act 7/1991, dated 30th April.

FERULA LINKII

Family
APIACEAE (PARSLEY)

Ferula linkii Webb.
Spanish common name: CAÑALEJA.

This Canary endemic occurs throughout the archipelago with the exception of Lanzarote. An annual, herbaceous, very robust species, it is characterised by its very tall, erect stems (which can be up to 3 m high). Reaching lengths of almost 1 metre, its large green leaves are divided into linear to filiform lobes. When in bloom, this is a truly spectacular plant, its small yellow flowers being arranged into tightly-packed terminal inflorescences over 10 cm in diameter. *Ferula linkii* flowers from late winter to early spring. It is typically found in sunny, exposed environments in medium-altitude and mountainous areas. The use of its leaves – crushed and applied in the form of a poultice – is recommended in the treatment of haemorrhoids.

Ferula linkii.

ARGYRANTHEMUN ADAUCTUM

Family
ASTERACEAE (DAISY)

Argyranthemun adauctum (Link) Humphr.

Taxonomically highly complex on account of its great morphological variability, 7 different subspecies have been described for this species, which is distributed amongst the islands of La Palma, El Hierro, Tenerife and Gran Canaria. As a rule, this is an evergreen, densely-branched shrub that grows to 1 metre in height and features hispid (bristly) stems. Measuring up to 8 cm long, its simple, alternate, sessile, obovate to rhomboidal leaves are divided –generally bi– or tripinnatifid – and overed in a layer of hair. Its flower eads, featuring white ligules and eing up to 1 cm in diameter, are rranged into 5 to 20 corymbose nflorescences. Its fruit is lacking 1 pappus. Very frequently found 1 the pinewoods and nountainous areas of the islands, nis species is protected under egional legislation, being listed in nnexe II of the Order regulating ne conservation of wild flora.

Argyranthemun adauctum.

ECHIUM ONOSMIFOLIUM

Family
BORAGINACEAE (FORGET-ME-NOT)

Echium onosmifolium Webb.
Spanish common name: TAJINASTE NEGRO (BLACK VIPER'S BUGLOSS).

xclusive to Gran Canaria, this black viper's bugloss is commonly found 1 the pinewoods and xeric areas lying at altitudes of between 400 and ,500 metres in the southern half of the island. A densely-branched hrub, it can grow up to 2 metres tall. Its pale green, linear to lanceolate, ery rough leaves measure up to 20 cm long and have entire, somewhat evolute margins. Covered in thick, large bristles above, their undersides eature short, simple hairs. *Echium onosmifolium* has an erect, narrow, ylindrical inflorescence which, up to 25 cm long, comprises numerous hitish, long-tubed, hort-lobed flowers. he plant blooms rom February to Iay and bears its ruit in the summer nonths. It is rotected under egional legislation Annexe II of the lora Order).

Echium onosmifolium.

CISTUS MONSPELIENSIS

Family
CISTACEAE (ROCKROSE)

Cistus monspeliensis L.
Spanish common name: JARA, JAGUARZO.

This widely distributed species native to the Mediterranean region is found on all the Canary Islands except for Fuerteventura and Lanzarote. A densely-branched, more or less globular evergreen shrub, it usually grows to a height of less than a metre. Its fragile branches are covered in a brown bark. The simple, entire, alternate, linear to lanceolate leaves are 4 to 5 cm long and are characterised by their revolute margins and very prominent veins. Narrow and rather sticky to the touch, they are dark green above and have a dense layer of hair (tomentum) underneath. A plant that blooms profusely, *Cistus monspeliensis* features highly delicate, ephemeral flowers comprising 5 white petals, amongst which a large cluster of bright yellow stamens is seen to stand out. Its fruit takes the form of small, valved capsules. Flowering individuals can be found practically all year round. A heliophilous (sun-loving) plant, it is typically found in areas that have witnessed the gradual disappearance of former pinewoods, often becoming the dominant species in degraded environments and acid substrata. Used medicinally in the form of infusions, the leaves and flowers of *Cistus monspeliensis* have pain and anxiety-relieving properties.

Cistus monspeliensis.

CISTUS SIMPHYTIFOLIUS

Family
CISTACEAE (ROCKROSE)

Cistus simphytifolius Lam.
Spanish common name: JARÓN, AMAGANTE.

Cistus simphytifolius.

. characteristic lement of the nderbrush of the 1ore or less well reserved Canary inewoods, this ndemic plant can be een on all the lands of the rchipelago except or Fuerteventura nd Lanzarote. A ifferent variety, *'istus leucophyllus,* has een described for ;ran Canaria. {eaching a height of p to 2 metres, *Cistus imphytifolius* is an vergreen shrub that aries in size and eatures densely rranged, fragile, rownish-grey ranches. Its simple, ntire, alternate, videly lanceolate eaves have rominent veins on heir undersides. Pale green in colour, the leaves are rough and sticky to he touch and are characterised by the thick layer of hair covering them, a eature which enables the plant to endure high temperatures and onditions of extreme drought. Reaching diameters of up to 5 cm, the lowers borne by this species are larger than those of *Cistus monspeliensis* nd are composed of 5 delicate, pinkish-coloured, ephemeral, papery etals. Standing out amidst the petals is a large cluster of bright yellow tamens. The fruits are hard, blackish capsules that on ripening open up nto 5 valves. Flowering above all in spring and summer, this plant is enowned for the pain-relieving properties of its leaves.

HELIANTHEMUN BYSTROPOGOPHYLLUM

Family
CISTACEAE (ROCKROSE)

⚠

Helianthemun bystropogophyllum Svent.
Spanish common name: TURMERO PELUDO.

  C

Helianthemun bystropogophyllum.

Endemic to Gran Canaria, this extremely rare species has been reported as existing in a single population in the south-western section of the island. A woody plant up to a metre in height, it features dense dichotomous branching. Measuring 3 to 5 cm long, its deciduous or subpersistent leaves are entire, oppositely-arranged, ovate-lanceolate and have highly prominent veins. The leaves are light green in colour and densely pubescent or hairy. *Helianthemun hystropogophyllum* has terminally arranged flowers about 2 cm across comprising 5 yellow petals and a central group of brighter-yellow stamens. Its capsular fruits are densely pubescent. The characteristic habitat of this species is the humid, shady rock walls within the limits of the pinewood formations. Due to the fact that only one population (containing very few individuals) remains, *Helianthemun hystropogophyllum* is on the verge of disappearing altogether. It is listed in Annexe I of the Berne Agreement and is regarded as a Priority Species in the EC Habitats Directive. On a national level, the plant is classified as a species "in danger of extinction" in the National Catalogue of Endangered Species, whilst it is subject to strict conservation measures under regional legislation.(Annexe I of the Flora Order).

ADENOCARPUS FOLIOLOSUS

Family
FABACEAE (PEA)

Adenocarpus foliolosus (Ait.) DC.
Spanish common name: CODESO (LABURNUM).

Adenocarpus foliolosus.

his shrub is widely distributed throughout the archipelago with the xception of Fuerteventura and Lanzarote. Two distinct varieties have een described, namely *Adenocarpus foliolosus,* which occurs on all the lands, and *Adenocarpus villosus,* restricted to Gran Canaria and La Palma. leafy, evergreen shrub standing from 2 to 4 metres high, it features a ense arrangement of spreading or arched branches. Its small, short-alked, divided leaves are trifoliolate, the dark green leaflets ranging in ape from lanceolate to obovate. The bright yellow flowers are grouped to terminal racemes and display a densely villous calyx and a sericious inely pubescent) standard petal. The fruits borne by *Adenocarpus liolosus* are narrowly oblong legumes featuring very few glands. This ecies is typically found amidst the pinewood underbrush, above all in e northern areas of the islands, and plays a vital role in re-colonising nds that have been ploughed up within the *monteverde* formations.

CHAMAECYTISUS PROLIFERUS

Family
FABACEAE (PEA)

Chamaecytisus proliferus (L. fil.) Link.
Spanish common name: ESCOBÓN, TAGASASTE.

Chamaecytisus proliferus.

This Canary endemic displays a high morphological variability, 4 distinct varieties having been described, all of which are distributed throughout the archipelago except for the islands of Fuerteventura and Lanzarote. Varying greatly in size, *Chamaecytisus proliferus* is a shrub that usually reaches heights of between 2 and 4 metres but occasionally stands as high as 7 metres. It features somewhat arched, densely-arranged branches. Trifoliolate and borne on long stalks, its leaves comprise lanceolate to ovate leaflets which, measuring up to 3 cm long, have entire margins and are covered on their underside with a fine layer of silvery hair. The flowers are arranged into axillary racemes of 1 to 4. They exhibit a tubular, short-lipped, deeply bilobed, reddish-hued, densely pubescent calyx accompanied by a white corolla. The fruit of *Chamaecytisus proliferus* is a somewhat curved, compressed, slightly villous legume that grows to lengths of up to 7 cm and turns black when ripe. Blooming above all in March and April, this plant forms mixed communities with pine-trees primarily in the southern regions of the islands, and in particular in some of the most humid areas of the latter. Moreover, it plays a vital role in colonising degraded pinewood environments. *Chamaecytisus proliferus* has been widely used by the rural population both as a fodder plant for livestock and in the production of farming tools and coal. Its use is regulated by the Flora Order (Annexe III species).

LOTUS BERTHELOTII

Family
FABACEAE (PEA)

Lotus berthelotii Masf.
Spanish common name: PICO DE PALOMA.

Lotus berthelotii.

his rare, beautiful species is endemic to the island of Tenerife and has a ighly restricted distribution. A subshrub-like creeping plant, it features ng, flexible, reclining or hanging branches that can reach lengths of ver 50 cm. Its long leaves comprise bundles of linear, up to 2 cm-long, eyish-green leaflets covered in silky hairs. The bright red flowers of *otus berthelotii,* grouped into fascicles of 2 to 4, are keel-shaped and come a long, prominent point. Its fruit is borne in pods measuring over 3 cm ng. For some time this species was believed to be extinct in its natural abitat and at present occurs in no more than two populations, each of hich contain very few individuals. Consequently, and bearing in mind e great difficulty the plant has in reproducing, the state of conservation f *Lotus berthelotii* is clearly to be defined as critical. Extensively used in the arks and gardens of the Canary Islands on account of its spectacular ooms and its value as a "carpeting" plant, this species is subject to strict onservation measures. It is classified as being "in danger of extinction" in e National Catalogue of Endangered Species and is protected under gional legislation (Annexe II of the Flora Order).

LOTUS HOLOSERICEUS

Family
FABACEAE (PEA)

Lotus holosericeus Webb et Berth.

Spanish common name: CORAZONCILLO, TREBOLILLO (TREFOIL).

Limited in distribution to central and southern Gran Canaria, this endemic is frequently found at altitudes of between 600 and 1,300 metres. It is a woody, prostrate, subshrub-like plant that forms more or less globular "cushions". It has divided, quinquefoliolate leaves whose greyish-green leaflets are linear to narrowly lanceolate in shape. The yellow inflorescences of *Lotus holosericeus* are racemes holding from 6 to 10 flowers each. An outstanding feature that distinguishes this plant from all similar species is the layer of long, silky hairs which, covering all its parts, lends it a certain silvery appearance. *Lotus holosericeus* blooms from March to May. Its habitat is basically that of scrublands dominated by other leguminous plants, open areas of pinewood, road and pathsides, etc. Despite being a locally abundant species, it inhabits only a restricted number of areas. Furthermore, it is regarded as "rare" in accordance with the categories laid down by the IUCN.

Lotus holosericeus.

LOTUS SPARTIOIDES

Family
FABACEAE (PEA)

Lotus spartioides Webb et Berth.
Spanish common name: CORAZONCILLO, TREBOLILLO DE PINAR (TREFOIL).

Lotus spartioides.

losely related to *Lotus holosericeus,* this species is endemic to the island of ran Canaria, where it occurs in pinewood areas at altitudes of over 000 metres. A small, semi-rounded, woody subshrub, it grows up to 40 cm ll, and has slender, suberect branches. Its leaves are divided into 5 more r less linear leaflets which are covered in a layer of short greyish hairs. porting a purple-edged calyx, the yellow flowers borne by *Lotus spartioides* e arranged into small racemes each holding 2 to 5 longly pedunculate owers. The fruit of this plant takes the form of a brownish-grey pod egume) measuring up to 1.5 cm long. Despite being a locally common ecies, it is nevertheless deemed to be rare on account of its very limited istribution (found only at a handful of sites in central Gran Canaria). It is rotected under regional legislation (Annexe II of the Flora Order).

ONONIS ANGUSTISSIMA

Family
FABACEAE (PEA)

Ononis angustissima Lam.
Spanish common name: MELOSILLA, MELOSA.

This widely distributed species is the centre of certain taxonomic debate, some authors reporting the existence of as many as 2 subspecie whilst others assign it the category of variety. Whatever the exact classification may be, however, the said subspecies or variety are in any case to be regarded as endemic to the Canary Islands, restricted as they are to Gran Canaria and Tenerife. A woody, evergreen plant, it is subshrub-like and densely branched. *Ononis angustissima* has dark green villous, very sticky, trifoliate leaves. The long, narrow leaflets feature joined stipules and veins that terminate in marginal teeth. Borne on long peduncles, the flowers exhibit a very divided calyx with more or less symmetrical teeth and a yellow, frequently red-striped corolla. *Ononis angustissima* has pods that measure up to 2.5 cm long and, like the leaves, are covered in long, soft hairs. Enjoying a wide distribution, this species occurs frequently above all on the southern slopes of the island, at altitudes of over 700 metres, where it is seen to belong to different plant communities. It is a plant that can occasionally induce allergy or irritation.

Ononis angustissima.

TELINE MICROPHYLLA

Family
FABACEAE (PEA)

Teline microphylla (DC.) Gibbs et Dingw.
Spanish common name: RETAMA AMARILLA (YELLOW BROOM).

Teline microphylla.

his spectacularly flowering broom is a very common sight in central and uthern regions of Gran Canaria, where it occurs at altitudes of between)0 and 1,900 metres. A woody, densely-branched, compact, evergreen rub, it grows to a height of up to 1 metre. Its young shoots have a silky pearance. The small, silvery-green, stalked, villous leaves are trifoliolate, mprising as they do 3 elliptic, tangled leaflets. The flowers of *Teline icrophylla* have a tubular, labiate, villous calyx featuring a two-toothed pper lip and a three-toothed lower lip. Atop the calyx lies the yellow-hued rolla, complete with its standard petal, which in this case is covered in ng, soft hairs at its apex. The flowers are grouped together into terminal r axillary racemes. So dense is the bloom of this plant that the latter ndergoes a considerable colour change during spring. The species rovides an abundant supply of fodder for rural communities, its use being gulated by the Flora Order (Annexe III).

GLOBULARIA ASCANII

Family
GLOBULARIACEAE (GLOBULARIA)

Globularia ascanii Bramw. et Kunk.

C

Globularia ascanii.

The sole habitat of this rare Canary endemic is the rocky, precipitous areas of north-western Gran Canaria. A woody shrub standing up to 80 cm tall, it densely-branched from its base and is classified as en evergreen, even thoug it loses most of its leaves during the less clement periods of the year. Its alternately arranged, long (5-10 cm), entire, dark green leaves are widely lanceolate, and somewhat fleshy in consistency. *Globularia ascanii* bears its flowers in globular heads on more or less long (up to 2 cm) terminal peduncles. Each of these flower heads is white, with a pale blue centre. The flowers feature a tubular, five-lobed calyx and a likewise tubular corolla in which two distinct labia are to be discerned: a shorter, two-lobed upper lip and a larger, three-lobed lower lip. *Globularia ascanii* produces a capsular fruit that holds a large number of seeds. Occurring in very few populations and having an extremely limited distribution, in keeping with the categorie established by the IUCN this species is to be regarded as being "endangered". Subject to strict protection measures, it is listed in Annexe I of the Berne Agreement and is considered a Priority Species in the EC Habitats Directive. Within the Spanish context, it is classified by the Nation Catalogue of Endangered Species as being "in danger of extinction" and is also deemed to merit particular protection under regional legislation (Annexe I of the Flora Order). This plant is closely related to another Canary endemic exclusive to Gran Canaria, *Globularia sarcophylla,* from whic it can be distinguished by its larger leaves and shorter peduncles, as well as the reclining posture adopted by the latter.

SATUREJA PINEOLENS

Family
LAMIACEAE (MINT)

Satureja pineolens (Svent.) Willemse.
Spanish common name: TOMILLO DEL PINAR.

. species endemic to Gran Canaria whose distribution is restricted to the umid pinewoods in the north-western region of the island, this woody, ensely branched bush ranks as one of the largest species of its genus, eaching a height of up to 80 cm. It displays a certain degree of ıorphological variability on account of the environmental conditions in hich it grows. Measuring up to 3 cm long, its lanceolate leaves are overed in long hairs on both sides and feature entire, revolute margins. *atureja pineolens* has relatively large flowers comprising a cylindrical, ɔng-haired, asymmetrically-toothed calyx and a tubular, bilabiate two-lipped), pink orolla. The lowers are rouped together t the ends of the ranches and are a rue spectacle vhen in bloom rom April to June.)espite being ocally abundant, n accordance with he IUCN ategories, this ɔlant is regarded s an 'endangered" pecies on account ɔf its limited ıumber of ɔopulations and ts restricted listribution. 'urthermore, it njoys strict ɔrotection neasures under egional egislation (Annexe I of the 'lora Order).

Satureja pineolens.

SATUREJA VARIA

Family
LAMIACEAE (MINT)

Satureja varia (Benth.) Webb et Berth. Ex Briq.
Spanish common name: TOMILLO (THYME).

Satureja varia.

This Canary endemic occurs on all the islands of the archipelago excep for La Palma. As a result of its high morphological variability, a total of seven subspecies and two varieties have been described. A dense, much-branched, subshrub-like plant, it grows up to 30 cm tall. It has small, linear to lanceolate leaves measuring under 1.5 cm which, usually not very hairy, are arranged in an opposite to fascicular fashion and display slightly revolute margins. The small flowers borne by *Satureja varia,* just 3-5 mm long, feature a green, cylindrical calyx with short, pointed teeth and a pink, tubular, bilabiate corolla. The flowers are grouped into loosely-arranged inflorescences in the from of short-stalked whorls. Found in abundance up to altitudes of around 2,000 metres, this specie is used as a condiment for food.

SIDERITIS DASYGNAPHALA

Family
LAMIACEAE (MINT)

Sideritis dasygnaphala (Webb et Berth.) Clos.
Spanish common name: SALVIA BLANCA (WHITE SALVIA, SAGE).

Sideritis dasygnaphala.

xclusive to Gran Canaria, this species abounds in the pinewood and
:guminous scrub areas occurring in the central regions of the island. A
oody, upright, much-branched subshrub, it has entire, simple, petiolate
:aves which, arranged alternately, are triangular-ovate or lanceolate in
hape and feature a rounded base and slightly dentate margins. The
hole plant is covered in a layer of white hair. *Sideritis dasygnaphala*
isplays inflorescences up to 20 cm long. Branched from their base, they
re more or less dense and comprise clustered whorls, each one of which
ontains a large number of flowers. Each whorl of flowers is encircled by
pair of petiolate, ovate linear or lanceolate bracts. Features of the
ıbular flowers are the long-spined teeth of the calyx and the yellow-
pped corolla. This species is extensively used by the local population on
ccount of its medicinal properties.

ASPHODELUS AESTIVUS

Family
LILIACEAE (LILY)

Asphodelus aestivus Brot.
Spanish common name: GAMONA (ASPHODEL).

Asphodelus aestivus.

Enjoying a wide distribution, this member of the lily family is found throughout the Canary archipelago. An herbaceous, perennial species it features a thick rhizome from which new growth appears each year. Grouped together in a basal rosette, its long, narrow, green leaves are V-shaped in section and terminate in a pointed tip. Arising from the centre of the rosette is the flowering stem, which can grow to a metre and a half tall. The spectacular white flowers of *Asphodelus aestivus* have a brown stripe in the middle of their petals and are borne on the stem in more or less dense racemes. Blooming above all in winter and spring, this species produces oval-shaped, reddish-coloured fruits. It displays a high ecological valence, abounding as it does in deforested areas and pasture lands, right from the lower-lying regions up to the open pinewood zones. The plant's rhizome has been used as a hair tonic (once boiled in water) and is recommended as a treatment for cysts and wounds (in poultice form).

Supracanary layer vegetation: Mountain-top scrub

As its name would suggest, mountain-top scrub occurs in the high mountains, at altitudes of over 2,000 metres, where climatic conditions are such that tree species are unable to prosper. This particular type of formation is limited to the islands of Tenerife and La Palma. On the former, the scrub is characterised by the prevalence of the brooms *(Spartocytisus supranubius)*, whereas the dominant species on the latter are the laburnums *(Adenocarpus viscosus* var. *spartioides)*, which constitute a compact, high-cover monospecific scrubland. Nevertheless, this species displays a greater altitudinal range and is seen to appear as from 800 metres.

These communities are of great importance due both to their use as a source of fodder during the spring and summer months and to the role they play in protecting the soils against erosion.

Appearing alongside the said dominant species is a series of other elements which are mostly endemics. Generally speaking, 80% of the plant species on this layer are endemic taxa, as a result of which these areas are deemed to be of particular scientific importance. Here we should highlight the presence of the "retamón" *(Genista benechoavensis* – an endangered species), as well as other interesting species such as *Pterocephalus porphyranthus,* thyme or "tomillo" *(Micromeria lasiophylla),* the El Teide stock or "alhelí del Teide" *(Erysimum scoparium), Nepeta teydea* and the red viper's bugloss or *Echium wildpretii.*

JUNIPERUS CEDRUS

Family
CUPRESSACEAE (CYPRESS)

Juniperus cedrus Webb et Berth.
Spanish common name: CEDRO CANARIO (CANARY CEDAR).

Juniperus cedrus.

This Macaronesian endemic, which yields a highly-valued wood, is found on Madeira and the islands of La Palma, La Gomera, Tenerife and Gran Canaria. A tree similar to the Mediterranean cedar, *Juniperus cedrus* stands up to 15 metres high, varies in size according to the environmental conditions in which it occurs, and has more or less hanging branches. The small, simple, entire, flat, dark green leaves of adult specimens are arranged either oppositely or in whorls and are linear-lanceolate or acicular in shape. A dioecious species, *Juniperus cedrus* has both male and female individuals. Borne in the axils of its leaves, the globular fruit measures 1 to 1.5 cm in diameter and turns a reddish hue on ripening. This is the only tree species found in the subalpine vegetation layer of the Canary Islands, appearing as it does in the highest-standing areas of pinewood and the high-mountain broom and laburnum formations of La Palma and Tenerife. The Canary cedar is also a common sight on La Gomera, whereas only a few specimens exist on Gran Canaria. In recent times the potential distribution of this tree has been dramatically reduced by forest fires and the felling of specimens for their highly-prized wood. *Juniperus cedrus* is protected under regional legislation (Annexe II of the Flora Order).

TOLPIS WEBBII

Family
ASTERACEAE (DAISY)

Tolpis webbii Sch. Bip. Ex Weeb et Berth.
Spanish common name: FLOR DE MALPAÍS.

Tolpis webbii.

'his species occurs more or less frequently in the Cañadas del Teide area
n the island of Tenerife, at an altitude of between 1,800 and 2,000 metres.
perennial, subshrub-like plant, it has a woody stem and is densely
ranched right from its base. Its rather villous, nearly erect, linear-
anceolate, dentate basal leaves are pinnatifid and unevenly lobed. Its
auline leaves (those growing on the upper part of the stem) are the same
hape as the basal ones but are smaller in size. *Tolpis webbii* has loosely-
rranged corymbose inflorescences, each flower stalk bearing 2 or 3 yellow
eads measuring approximately 1 cm in diameter. Characteristic of the
ıalpais (bad land) environments, this plant is commonly found on
recipitous terrain and in areas of pumice stone.

ECHIUM WILDPRETII

Family
BORAGINACEAE (FORGET-ME-NOT)

Echium wildpretii Pears. ex Hook fil.
Spanish common name: TAJINASTE ROJO, TAJINASTE DE LAS CAÑADAS.

Echium wildpretii.

This singularly beautiful viper's bugloss is found at altitudes of between 1,600 and 2,000 metres on the islands of Tenerife and La Palma. Two subspecies have been described, namely *Echium wildpretii* for Cañadas del Teide on Tenerife and *Echium trichosiphon* for the steeply-sloping terrain of La Caldera de Taburiente on La Palma. A characteristic feature of this perennial shrub is the arrangement of its basal leaves into a rosette measuring up to 1 metre across. Its large, elongated, linear leaves are covered in a thick layer of long bristles. Arising from the centre of the basal rosette is the plant's inflorescence which, standing up to 3 metres high, is composed of thousands of bright red flowers. The flowers comprise a five-lobed calyx and a funnel-shaped corolla, from which five stamens project out. The fruit borne by *Echium wildpretii* is a small nut that is rough to the touch. Flowering in late spring and early summer, this viper's bugloss is widely planted in the parks and gardens of the Canaries on account of its spectacular bloom. It enjoys protection under regional legislation (Annexe II of the Flora Order).

ERYSIMUM SCOPARIUM

Family

BRASSICACEAE (MUSTARD)

Erysimum scoparium (Brouss. ex Willd.) Wettst.
Spanish common name: ALHELÍ DEL TEIDE (EL TEIDE STOCK).

Erysimum scoparium.

'axonomically speaking this is a very complex Canary endemic. Most uthors acknowledge the presence of this species on the islands of La 'alma, Tenerife and Gran Canaria. The variety *Erisum cinereus* has been lescribed for Tenerife, whilst the subspecies *lindleyi* is found on Gran 'anaria. A small, shrubby, densely-branched evergreen, it features erect tems and a greyish bark. Its entire, very narrow, alternately arranged, reyish-green, linear to linear-lanceolate leaves measure up to 8 cm long, re rough to the touch and are covered with soft, short, unbranched airs. The leaf margins vary in form from entire to slightly dentate. *'rysimum scoparium* has small, regular flowers whose tubular calyx omprises 4 violet-coloured lobes. Projecting out from its corolla - composed of 4 unjoined petals varying in colour from white to shades f violet – are 6 stamens complete with magnificent yellow anthers. The ruit produced by this plant is a brown, more or less erect, cylindrical apsule called a siliqua. Flowering in spring, this species contains ubstances that display cardiotonic properties.

SPARTOCYTISUS SUPRANUBIUS

Family
FABACEAE (PEA)

Spartocytisus supranubius (L. fil.) Weeb et Berth.
Spanish common name: RETAMA BLANCA, RETAMA DEL TEIDE.

Spartocytisus supranubius.

This broom is one of the dominant species of the high mountain scrub formations occurring at altitudes of between 2,000 and 2,200 metres. Commonly found on the island of Tenerife, it is more sparsely distributed on La Palma. A densely-branched shrub growing to a height of up to 3 metres, it usually takes on a hemispherical shape. Growing on its erect, greyish-hued branches are small, deciduous, ephemeral, nearly sessile, trifoliolate leaves whose linear, pale green leaflets measure under 5 mm long. *Spartocytisus supranubius* bears flowers that are grouped together into dense racemes at the ends of the branches. Shortly petiolate, they feature a bilabiate, very short-toothed calyx and a white or pink corolla. The fruit of this broom takes the form of black, 4 to 6-seeded, villous legumes. It is a highly aromatic plant when in bloom (May to July). This species is protected under regional legislation (Annexe II of the Flora Order).

NEPETA TEYDEA

Family
LAMIACEAE (MINT)

Nepeta teydea Webb et Berth.
Spanish common name: HIERBA DEL TEIDE, TONÁTICA, HIERBA GATERA, NEUTA

his species is found only on Tenerife and La Palma, at altitudes of 1,800-,000 metres. Two separate varieties have been described, namely *Nepeta teydea,* hich occurs on both islands; and the white-flowered *Nepeta albiflora,* which is estricted to Tenerife. An herbaceous, basally woody perennial, it is densely ranched and grows up to a metre and a half tall. Its simple, oppositely-rranged, oblong-lanceolate, hairy leaves are up to 5 cm long and have oarsely dentate margins. The flowers of this plant are over 4 mm long and xhibit a purple, five-toothed tubular calyx with 15 veins. The likewise tubular, urved corolla is violet-coloured and bilabiate. Whereas the upper lip of the orolla is bilobed, the lower one is trilobed, its middle lobe being longer than he side ones. The flowers borne by *Nepeta teydea* are grouped together into a uccession of whorls that give rise to a spike-shaped inflorescence. This species s protected under regional legislation (Annexe II of the Flora Order).

Nepeta teydea.

ARRHENATHERUM CALDERAE

Family
POACEAE (GRASS)

Arrhenatherum calderae A Hans.

Arrhenatherum calderae

Although this gramineous species is locally abundant, its distribution is restricted to Las Cañadas del Teide, Tenerife. A perennial, lawny grass, it grows up to a metre high. Its stems are the same thickness in each of their internodes. *Arrhenatherum calderae* bears loosely-arranged, much-branched inflorescences. Its spikelets contain two small flowers, the lower one of which features an almost straight awn during anthesis (the flowering period). The outer scales or glumes of the spikelets are almost identical, the lower glume displaying just one vein in comparison to the upper one, which has three. This grass has two-toothed, seven-ribbed lamma and its whitish-yellow anthers

Rock Communities

The geographical relief of the Canary Islands favours the establishment of rock ommunities comprising plants that are especially adapted to survive in the xtreme conditions that prevail on the numerous escarpments and walls of rock be observed right from the very coast up to the mountain peaks. These areas ave come to constitute veritable refuges for many of the islands' endemic pecies. Indeed, it should come as no surprise that it is precisely on these crags nd sheer rock faces that most of the floristic diversity of the Canaries is to be ncountered. This is the case of the craggy landscapes at Famara on Lanzarote; andía on Fuerteventura; Tenteniguada, Tirajana and Andén Verde on Gran anaria; at Anaga on Tenerife; El Golfo on El Hierro; at Taburiente on La Palma; nd the precipitous terrain at Garajonay on La Gomera.

ock vegetation on the Canaries displays a pattern of variation governed by limatic and altitudinal differences, as a result of which different types of ommunities are to be identified. Thus, the rock communities found on oastal cliffs and escarpments – directly influenced by the sea environment – xhibit certain characteristics all of their own and, dominated by species elonging to the halophilic belt, also feature a considerable variety of lichens. greater variety and density of species is to be seen on the crags and scarpments of the transitional, montane and basal layers, which contain umerous endemic taxa, most of the species found pertaining to the genera *eonium, Greenovia, Aichrysum, Sonchus* and *Carlina.* Particularly oteworthy are the rock communities that appear in high mountain areas, nsofar as they display many highly-prized endemics such as the viper's ugloss *Echium gentianoides.*

SONCHUS ACAULIS

Family
ASTERACEAE (DAISY)

Sonchus acaulis Dum.-Cours.
Spanish common name: CERRAJÓN.

Sonchus acaulis.

Restricted to Tenerife and Gran Canaria, this Canary endemic is characteristic of the precipitous areas and rocky slopes of the mid-altitude regions of both islands and is also found to grow on the roof-tops of houses. A basally woody perennial, its unbranched, thick trunk can reach a height of up to 1 metre. Grouped together in a large rosette up to a metre across, its simple, somewhat tomentose, green leaves are lanceolate, pinnately divided and up to 60 cm long. The flowering stalk or scape of *Sonchus acaulis* is leafless and can grow to over 1 metre. Its flowers are arranged at the end of the scape into umbellate inflorescences bearing only a few heads. The yellow heads measure up to 2.5 cm across, although when completely open they can reach a diameter of over 8 cm. This species also features broad whorled bracts with a dense layer of white hair.

SONCHUS BRACHYLOBUS

Family
ASTERACEAE (DAISY)

Sonchus brachylobus Weeb et Berth.
Spanish common name: CERRAJÓN DE RISCO.

Sonchus brachylobus.

redominantly a rock species, this plant is commonly found in northern
nd western Gran Canaria at altitudes of between 200 and 600 metres. Two
rieties have been identified, namely *Sonchus brachylobus* and *Sonchus*
mariae, the leaves of the latter possessing pointed lobes. An evergreen
oody perennial, it is irregularly branched and grows up to 80 cm high. Its
ranches are knotty and scarred. Arranged into more or less terminal
settes, the simple, light green, lyrate-pinnatisect leaves measure up to
2 cm long, are somewhat fleshy, have a denticulate margin and feature a
rminal lobe that is larger than those flanking it. *Sonchus bracylobus* has a
ort, flowery stem (scape) bearing only a few yellow flower heads up to
cm in diameter. It flowers from April to May.

SONCHUS CANARIENSIS

Family
ASTERACEAE (DAISY)

Sonchus canariensis (Sch. Bip.) Boulos.
Spanish common name: CERRAJA (SOW THISTLE).

Exclusive to Tenerife and Gran Canaria, this Canary endemic has two subspecies, namely *Sonchus canariensis,* which is found on both islands; and *Sonchus orotavensis,* itself restricted to the island of Tenerife. An evergreen, woody perennial standing up to 3 metres high, it features fragile, irregularly-arranged, up-turned slender branches. Its leaves are grouped into rosettes near the base of the stem. Measuring up to 40 cm long, they are simple, lanceolate, light green, pinnatisect leaves with a varying number of lobes arranged in 10 to 15 pairs.
The terminal, much-branched, rather dense inflorescences of *Sonchus canariensis* are composed of yellow flower heads up to 4 cm in diameter. Flowering from March to May, this rock species is typically found in mid-altitude regions (200-800 metres) of northern and western Tenerife and Gran Canaria.

Sonchus canariensis.

SONCHUS CONGESTUS

. *Family*
ASTERACEAE (DAISY)

ionchus congestus Willd.
panish common name: CERRAJA (SOW THISTLE).

Sonchus congestus.

vo separate varieties have been described for this species, which is only to be und on Tenerife and Gran Canaria. Whereas *Sonchus congestus* occurs on th islands, *Sonchus gibbosus* is exclusive to Gran Canaria. An evergreen rennial reaching heights of up to 2 metres, it displays fragile, densely-ranged, slender branches. Its leaves are grouped into rosettes near the base the stem. Measuring up to 30 cm long, they are simple, lanceolate, nnatifid leaves featuring serrate margins and lobes that taper to a sharp int. The relatively small, umbellate, terminal inflorescences of *Sonchus ngestus* comprise a short scape or flower stalk bearing yellow, tomentose ads from 2 to 2.5 cm in diameter. Widely distributed on Tenerife at altitudes between 800 and 1,500 metres, this rock species is not so common on Gran naria, being restricted to the northern and central regions of the island.

VIERAEA LAEVIGATA

Family
ASTERACEAE (DAISY)

Vieraea laevigata (Brouss. ex Willd.) Webb.
Spanish common name: AMARGOSA.

C

The only species of its genus, this subshrub-like plant is endemic to the island of Tenerife. Standing up to a metre high, it is densely branched and features fragile, slender greyish-coloured stems. Its simple, alternat bluish-green fleshy leaves are rather large (5-8 cm), widely lanceolate ar cover the entire length of the stem. The leaf margins are dentate, above all towards the apex. *Vieraea laevigata* has somewhat dense, terminal inflorescences comprising 5 to 10 large bright-yellow heads that vary in diameter from 2 to 3 cm. The flower pedicels are densely bracted. Flowering in spring and summer, this rare xerophilous rock species is found in the mountainous regions of north-western Tenerife, where it grows on basaltic crags at altitudes of between 50 and 500 metres. The plant is named after one of the great scholars in the field of Canary flora, José de Viera y Clavijo, who showed a specia interest in the natur history of these islands, a vocation which led to the publication of his "Dictionary of the Natural History of tl Canary Islands" in 1866, the oldest botanical document to have been written on the archipelago. It is a scientifically highly interesting species on account c its being the only species of its genus. It enjoys protection under regional legislation (Annexe of the Flora Order).

Vieraea laevigata.

AEONIUM MANRIQUEORUM

Family
CRASSULACEAE (STONECROP)

eonium manriqueorum Bolle.
panish common name: HIERBA PUNTERA.

C

Aeonium manriqueorum.

is species is very commonly found in the rocky, precipitous regions of rthern and central Gran Canaria, at altitudes of between 200 and 200 metres. It is a branched, succulent, perennial shrub that reaches a ight of up to 1 metre. Its cylindrical fleshy stems are characterised by e scars left by fallen leaves. Arranged in terminal rosettes measuring -20 cm across, the flat, spatulate, fleshy leaves are a lustrous green lour and feature a reddish, ciliate margin, the cilia (hair-like ocesses) of which pointing towards the apex of the leaf. Borne apically the branches, the magnificent showy inflorescences of *Aeonium nriqueorum* contain a multitude of yellow flowers. The flowering stems ve obovate or oblong, sparsely-arranged leaves. This plant blooms from ne to September. It is protected under regional legislation. (Annexe II the Flora Order).

AEONIUM SIMSII

Family

CRASSULACEAE (STONECROP)

Aeonium simsii (Sw.) Stearn.

Spanish common name: CÓNGANO, FLOR DE PIEDRA.

This highly abundant species is very widely distributed, occurring as it does from an altitude of 600 metres above sea level right up to the mountain peaks of Gran Canaria. A succulent perennial plant, it affords a lawny appearance. Grouped into very dense basal rosettes measuring 5-8 cm in diameter, the linear-lanceolate to narrowly oblong, fleshy, green red-striped leaves are densely ciliate, featuring long, diaphanous hair-like processes. On their undersides the leaves exhibit a number of prominent glands. The erect, reddish flowering stems rise to a height of 20 cm from the rosette and bear small, likewise narrow, reddish leaves. *Aeonium simsii* has a small, umbellate inflorescence composed of yellow flowers 1 cm in diameter. Flowering from March to June, as is the case with the rest of the endemics belonging to this genus, this taxon is protected under regional legislation (Annexe II of the Flora Order).

Aeonium simsii.

AEONIUM TABULAEFORME

Family

CRASSULACEAE (STONECROP)

eonium tabulaeforme Weeb et Berth.

panish common name: PASTEL DE RISCO, GÓNGANO, YERBA PUNTERA.

Aeonium tabulaeforme.

his locally abundant species endemic to Tenerife is found above all on
e crags and precipitous terrain of the north-western region of the
and. Generally occurring singly, it is a succulent perennial somewhat
erbaceous in appearance. Its densely imbricated (overlapping) leaves
rm a flat, sessile, tightly-packed rosette ranging in diameter from 30 to
 cm. The pale green, more or less spatulate leaves have margins
inged with long cilia. *Aeonium tabulaeforme* has erect flowering stems
ith oblong scales that are bilobed at the apex. Its inflorescences are
mposed of a large number of small, star-shaped, yellow flowers.
owering in summer, this highly ornamental plant ranks as one of the
ost singular species of its genus. The extract obtained by crushing its
aves is recommended for the treatment of burns and has an analgesic
fect on surface wounds. This species is protected under regional
gislation. (Annexe II of the Flora Order).

GREENOVIA AUREA

Family
CRASSULACEAE (STONECROP)

Greenovia aurea (Chr. Sm. ex Hornem.) Weeb et Berth.
Spanish common name: PASTEL DE RISCO, BEJEQUE, SANJORA.

Greenovia aurea.

This Canary endemic occurs on all the islands of the archipelago except for Fuerteventura and Lanzarote. It is a succulent, short-stemmed perennial. Its basal rosettes measure up to 25 cm across and comprise thick, fleshy, densely-imbricated leaves. More or less spatulate, the leaves are a bluish-green (glaucous) colour with tinges of red and have non-ciliate margins. A large number of very showy yellow flowers grow at the top of the flowering stems of *Greenovia aurea* which, up to 40 cm tall, are clothed in imbricated leaves. This species blooms in spring and is protected under regional legislation (Annexe II of the Flora Order).

GREENOVIA DIPLOCYCLA

Family
CRASSULACEAE (STONECROP)

Greenovia diplocycla Weeb ex Bolle.
Spanish common name: BEJEQUE, SANJORA.

This Canary endemic is found on the islands of La Palma, La Gomera and El Hierro. It is a succulent, very short-stemmed species whose leaves are grouped together into tightly-packed, isolated basal rosettes measuring up to 20 cm in diameter. Its fleshy, thick, bluish-green leaves are more or less spatulate in shape. The yellow flowers of this plant are grouped into inflorescences on a long flowering stem that arises from the centre of the rosette. Flowering in spring, this species can be distinguished from *Greenovia aurea* by its subtly ciliate leaf margins and the absence of any side rosettes. It is characteristic of the humid environments of the lower-lying and mid-altitude regions of the islands on which it occurs. It enjoys protection on a regional scale, being listed in Annexe II of the Flora Order.

Greenovia diplocycla.

APPENDICES

BIBLIOGRAPHICAL REFERENCES

AMWELL, D. & Z. BRAMWELL, 1990:
ores silvestres de las Islas Canarias.
litorial Rueda. Madrid.

ÓMEZ CAMPO, C. & COLABORADORES, 1996:
bro Rojo de Especies Vegetales Amenazadas de las Islas Canarias.
ceconsejería de Medio Ambiente, Consejería de Política Territorial y
edio Ambiente del Gobierno de Canarias.

ONZÁLEZ HENRÍQUEZ, M. N., J. RODRIGO PÉREZ & C. SUÁREZ RODRÍGUEZ, 1986:
ora y vegetación del archipiélago Canario.
lirca. Las Palmas de Gran Canaria.

JNKEL, G. & M. A. KUNKEL, 1978:
ora de Gran Canaria. III.
s Plantas suculentas. Cabildo Insular de Gran Canaria. Las Palmas.

JNKEL, G., 1991:
ora y vegetación del archipiélago Canario.
atado Florístico 2ª Parte. Edirca. Las Palmas de Gran Canaria.

GLOSSARY OF BOTANICAL TERMS

Alternate leaves: Leaves arranged one after the other along the stem in a helicoidal fashion.

Angiosperm: One of the two major divisions of the spermatophytes. Plants featuring covered seeds or true fruits that contain (cover) the seed.

Anther: The part of the stamen that develops and contains pollen.

Antipyretic: A substance used to reduce fever.

Apical: Of, relating to or situated at an apex. Located at the distal end.

Arcéstidas: Spanish name given to the berry-like, indehiscent fleshy fruit that i typical of the *Juniperus* genus and comprises knitted scales.

Arista: A bristle-like tuft or appendage.

Astringent: Agent or substance able to draw together the soft organic tissues an to reduce secretions.

Awn: One of the slender bristles that terminate the glumes of the spikelet in some grasses.

Axil: The upper angle between a leaf or bract and the stem from which it arises

Axillary: Located at (situated in or growing from) the axils.

Bark: Tough exterior covering of woody plant stems.

Berry: A fleshy indehiscent fruit comprising more than two carpels and numerous seeds.

Bilabiate: Having two lips.

Bioclimatic: Relating to the analysis and study of the climate in relation to flora and fauna.

Biogeographical region: Any geographical area that is characterised by a distin flora and fauna.

Boreal Realm: One of the six major phytogeographical areas of the planet characterised by its particular flora. This realm comprises the American North Atlantic, the Arctic and Subarctic, the Eurosiberian, the Macaronesian, the Mediterranean, the North Pacific, the Sino-Japanese and the Western and Central Asian floristic regions.

Bract: A leafy organ – different from normal leaves – situated at the base of the flower or encircling the latter.

Bryological: Relating to the mosses (Musci) and the liverworts (Hepaticae).

Calyx: The outer whorl of the perianth in a flower, formed by usually green, herbaceous sepals.

Capitulum, (pl. Capitula): Inflorescence composed of non-pedunculate flowers arranged on a flattened floral axis or receptacle. Characteristic of the Asterace (Daisy) family.

Capsular: Of, being or relating to a capsule.

Capsule: Dry, indehiscent fruit formed by the fusion of two or more carpels an containing numerous seeds.

arina: The keel-shaped lower fused petals of the flowers of the leguminous plants.

arpel: Transformed leaf forming the ovary of flowering plants.

haracter: Any distinctive trait or attribute of an organism that constitutes the asis for its comparison.

iliate: Provided with cilia.

ilium (pl. Cilia): A minute, short hairlike process often forming a fringe.

ladode, Cladophyll: Specialised branch or stem assuming the form of a leaf nd performing the functions of the latter.

limax community: A more or less stable biotic community that has reached a ate of equilibrium with the prevailing environmental conditions and which onstitutes the final stage of an ecological succession.

limbing plant: A plant that climbs or ascends by twining around trees or any her object.

ommunity: Any grouping of organisms belonging to several different species at live together in the same habitat or area and interact by way of trophic and atial relations. As a rule, the community will be characterised by the existence f one or more dominant species.

ompound leaves: Leaves whose blades are divided into several distinct leaflets that e joined to the central axis (or rachis) by means of small petioles or leaf stalks.

onifers: An order (Coniferales) of woody, usually arboreal plants including ines, firs, spruces, cedars, cypresses and junipers.

ordate: Shaped like a heart.

ordiform: Heart-shaped.

orolla: The inner whorl of the perianth (in complete flowers) situated etween the calyx and the reproductive organs, consisting of generally brightly oloured petals.

reeper: Plant that grows along the ground or any substratum.

renulate: Having notches or small indentations on the leaf margin.

yme: Inflorescence whose central axis terminates in a single flower, as do all e secondary axes arising from it.

ypsela: Dry, indehiscent fruit typical of the Asteraceae that is derived from an ferior ovary and is formed by two carpels and a single seed.

eciduous: Species or communities of trees or shrubs that shed their leaves uring the most adverse seasons.

ehiscence: Spontaneous opening of ripe plant structures in order to liberate eds or spores.

entate: Used to describe a leaf whose margin features tooth-shaped rojections.

enticulate: (Of a leaf margin) Finely dentate.

ioecious: Unisexual, male and female flowers being borne separately on ifferent individuals.

Diversity: Absolute number or species richness of an assemblage, community or sample.

Drupe: Fleshy, single-seeded indehiscent fruit comprising one or two carpels.

Ecological Valence: Range of intrinsic properties and conditioning factors that determine the distribution of a plant.

Ecosystem: A community of organisms and its physical environment functionin as an ecological unit in nature.

Edaphic: Of or relating to the nature of the soil or influenced by the latter.

Endemic: Native to a specific geographical area and restricted to it.

Fascicle: A compact grouping of leaves or flowers.

Filiform: Thin and fine, shaped like a filament or thread.

Floristic companion species: Ensemble of plant species accompanying the principal species of an association.

Floristic: Of or relating to flora or the plant species that make up the vegetatior of a given area or region.

Flower head; Head: Inflorescence whose flowers, which are sessile or have a very short peduncle, are inserted in a receptacle, itself normally surrounded by bract

Flowering stem, floriferous stem: Stem bearing the flowers or inflorescences of a plant.

Fodder plant: Plant species used as food for grazing animals.

Foliolate: Having (such or so many) leaflets; eg. *quinquefoliolate (pentafoliado).*

Follicle: Dry, indehiscent fruit that opens along only the dorsal suture.

Fruit: Product of the development of a plant ovary subsequent to fertilisation.

Glabrous: Lacking in hair.

Glandular: Displaying excrescences or glands.

Glaucous: Of a light green colour, with a slightly bluish hue.

Gymnosperms: One of the two major divisions of the spermatophytes which includes all conifer species.

Habitat: The place, site and particular type of local environment occupied by an organism.

Herbaceous: Having the characteristics and qualities of a herb; non-woody.

Herbs: Small, non-woody, generally annual plants, all the parts of which display soft consistency.

Horizontal precipitation: Precipitation produced by the condensation of airborne moisture on the leaves of trees. A characteristic phenomenon of the laurisilva (laurel) and pinewood formations.

Hydric stress: Critical situation in the survival of a species caused by a lack of wate

Inflorescence: A grouping or arrangement of flowers characterised by a particular system of branching.

Laciniate: Deeply cut into irregular, narrow, usually pointed lobes.

Lanceolate: Shaped like a lance head.

Latex: A characteristic fluid – complex and varied in composition – that circulates around the lactiferous vessels of many plants.

Laurisilva: The name given to what is the most richly varied plant formation to be found on the Canary Islands, a humid woodland comprising laurels and other related genera.

Leaflet: Each of the divisions or small leaves that go to make up a compound leaf.

Leathery: Resembling leather in appearance or consistency; tough, displaying mechanical properties similar to those of leather, that is, thick but flexible to a degree.

Legume: A dry, dehiscent fruit (pod) composed of a single carpel and a variable number of seeds, typical of leguminous plants.

Lemma: The lower of the two bracts enclosing the flower in the spikelet of grasses.

Liana: Climbing, woody plant.

Lianoid: Resembling a liana in appearance.

Ligule (Ligulate or Ray Floret): Name given to each of the exterior gamopetalous and zygomorphic flowers of the capitulum in composites.

Linear: (of leaves) Long and narrow with more or less parallel margins.

Lip: Name given to each of the two parts into which the corolla is divided in certain flowers. In the family of the labiates, the upper lip comprises two petals whereas the lower one features three.

Lobe: Each of the rounded, projecting divisions of a leaf or the flowers of a plant.

Loculus: Cavity or chamber of any plant organ, generally that of a fruit (pl., loculi).

Lyrate: Having or suggesting the shape of a lyre.

Macaronesian Region: Subdivision of the boreal biogeographical realm comprising the archipelagos of the Canaries, the Azores, Madeira and Cape Verde along with a short, narrow coastal strip of Northern Africa.

Membranous: Resembling membrane, thin and smooth.

Monteverde: A formation of generally evergreen shrubs and small trees. Blanket term used to refer jointly to the *laurisilva* (laurel forest) and *fayal-brezal* (heather and myrtle) formations.

Morphological: Relating to the form and structure of individual organisms, above all their external features.

Nectary: Plant glands that secrete nectar.

Niche: A term referring to the position occupied by a species and which encompasses both the physical area in which a given species lives and the functional role it plays.

Nitrophile: Plant that grows in soils rich in nitrogen-containing compounds.

Notch: Semicircular cut, concavity or gap in the leaves or stems of plants.

Oblanceolate: Inversely lanceolate, that is, lance-shaped leaves that taper towards the base.

Oligospecific: Used to denote a community characterised by the presence and/or dominance of a small number of species.

Orbicular, orbiculate: Circular, spherical (used to refer to fruit or leaf shape).

Ovate: Oval-shaped.

Panicle: A compound racemose inflorescence featuring unequally pedunculate flowers.

Pappus: (plural, pappi) An appendage of hairs or threads that crowns the fruit of many plants of the Compositae family and which functions in the airborne dispersal of the fruit.

Pedicel: Stalk of an individual flower in compound inflorescences.

Pedicellate: Having a pedicel.

Peduncle: Stalk that supports an individual flower or an inflorescence.

Perennial: Lasting. Used to refer to plants that persist for several years and have a period of new growth each year.

Perianth: The external envelope of a flower comprising both the petals and the sepals.

Petal: A modified leaf, normally brightly or vividly coloured, that forms part of the corolla of a flower.

Petiole: Leaf stalk joining the leaf blade with the stem.

Pinna: (pl.: Pinnae): A primary division, or leaflet, of a compound leaf.

Pinnately divided: Used to describe a divided leaf or leafy organ whose incisions go beyond the centre of each half of the blade but do not reach the midrib.

Pinnatifid: Used to describe a leaf or leafy organ cleft into segments whose incisions at the most extend halfway to the midrib.

Pinnatisect: Used to describe a deeply cut leaf whose incisions reach the midrib. Depending on the number of incisions present, the leaf is referred to as bipinnatisect, tripinnatisect, and so on.

Primocoloniser: Any of the first species that successfully invade (colonise) a new habitat.

Procumbent: Having stems that trail along the ground.

Pubescent: Having fine, short, soft hairs.

Pyrophilous: Used to refer to a plant that grows in soils that have recently been affected by fire.

Pyrophyte: Plant adapted to withstand fire.

Raceme: A simple, elongated inflorescence featuring stalked flowers at different heights, the oldest being at the base – *adj., racemose.*

Relict: Used to refer to plants or plant communities whose former distribution was much wider than today.

Resin: Solid or semisolid substance, soluble in alcohol but not in water, that is derived from the compounds flowing through the vessels of a plant.

Revolute: Rolled backwards or downwards (eg., leaf margin).

Rhizome: Underground stem.

Rocky plant: Plant that lives amidst rocks or on walls of rock.

Rosette-shaped: Having the form of a rosette.

Ruderal: Used to denote a species capable of growing on waste or detritus or which colonises environments disturbed by man.

Sap: Liquid that circulates through the vascular system of pteridophytes and phanerogams and from which plant cells take the nutritional substances they need.

Scape: A peduncle arising at or beneath the level of the ground; a flower stalk.

Scar: Mark left on plant tissues after an injury has healed.

Sea of clouds: Phenomenon caused by the condensation of the moisture borne by the Trade Winds current, which on striking the northern and north-eastern slopes of the Canary Islands rises abruptly and is cooled, thus giving rise to low cloud and horizontal precipitation. This atmospheric phenomenon occurs at altitudes of between 500 and 1,200 m, depending on the island concerned, its orientation and the time of year.

Seed: The fertilised ripened ovule of a flowering plant.

Seminatural: (Used of plant communities): modified by human influence.

Sericeous: Covered with fine short hairs that have a silky sheen.

Serrate: Having pointed marginal teeth arranged in close succession – saw-toothed, syn.

Sessile: Lacking in peduncles or stalks.

Sparse: Not thickly grown or settled, not densely arranged.

Spatulate: Shaped like a spatula.

Spike: Unbranched inflorescence featuring more or less sessile flowers, the oldest of which being situated at the base.

Spur: Tubular prolongation situated at the base of some flowers, sometimes in the corolla, other times in the calyx.

Stamen: The male organ of a flower of the phanerogams (spermatophytes) that is a modified leaf and consists of an anther (where the pollen is located) and the filament supporting it.

Staminal column: Name given to the tube made up of the stamens of the Malvaceae family.

Staminal: Of or relating to a stamen.

Standard petal: The large odd upper petal of papilionaceous flower (e.g the pea).

Stem: Primary plant axis that grows away from the roots and serves as a support for leaves, flowers and fruit.

Stigma: Glandular body situated at the tip of the pistil of a flower, which receives the pollen in plant fertilisation.

Style: Hollow, spongy column present in most flowers which, arising from the top of the ovary, supports the stigma.

Subsessile: Nearly sessile.

Subshrub: A plant of virtually the same proportions and characteristics as a shrub; a low shrub.

Substratum, Substrate: Surface or medium on which a plant grows.

Succulent: Plant featuring specialised fleshy tissues in its roots, leaves or stems designed to conserve water.

Támaras: Name given to the ovoidal, orangish fruits of the Canary palm *(Phoenix canariensis),* which are smaller than dates.

Taxon: Any group of organisms or populations held to be sufficiently distinct from other similar groups in order to be regarded as constituting a separate taxonomic unit.

Terminal: Situated or growing at the end of a branch or a stem of a plant.

Thermophile: An organism growing in hot environmental conditions – *thermophilous, adj.*

Thermosclerophyllous: Used to refer to plant formations comprising species that grow in hot temperatures and feature hard, sclerotic leaves.

Thorn: Pointed process that springs from the woody or vascular tissue of certain plants.

Thorny: Having spines or thorns.

Trilobed: Having three lobes.

Tomentose: Covered with densely cottony, pubescent or finely matted hairs.

Tomentum: Layer of hairs covering the surface of the organs of certain plants.

Umbel: Dorsally flattened inflorescence characteristic of the Umbelliferae (carrot) family, featuring flower stalks (pedicels) of more or less the same length that arise from a common point, thus lending it the appearance of an umbrella.

Underbrush: Shrubby vegetation that grows beneath large trees in a wood or forest.

Valve: Each of the segments into which a dehiscing capsule or pod breaks up on ripening.

Vegetation layer: A horizontal layer or stratum which, situated between two given altitudes, is characterised by the presence of a particular plant community and is conditioned by the bioclimatic factors prevailing at that height.

Vein: A vascular fibrous bundle which, taking the shape of a thread or filament, runs along the underside of a leaf, normally standing out above the surface.

Venation, Nervation: Arrangement or system of veins in a leaf.

Villous: Having long, silky hairs.

Wood: Relatively large area featuring arboreal plant species growing close to each other.

Woody: Shrubs, plants, fruits, etc. that have the consistency and hardness of wood.

Xeric: used to refer to a dry, as opposed to a wet (hydric) environment.

Xerophyte: A plant that can live in dry habitats and generally features adaptations that enable it to withstand long periods of drought.

INDEXES

ALPHABETICAL INDEX OF FAMILIES

COASTAL HALOPHILIC VEGETATION

BASAL-LAYER COMMUNITIES

ALPHABETICAL INDEX OF PLANTS

GENERAL INDEX OF CONTENTS

Pag

CANARY

LA PALMA

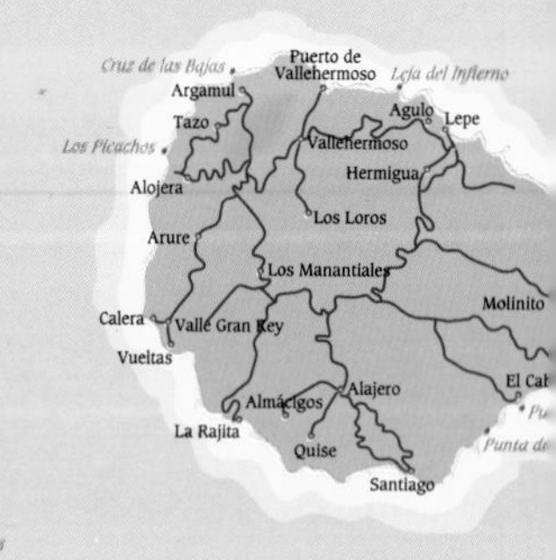

LA GOM

EL HIERRO